Wisdom of the Earth Speaks

The Truth About Medicinal Aromatherapy

Wisdom of the Earth Speaks
The Truth About Medicinal Aromatherapy
by Barry B. Kapp

Published by
Barry B. Kapp
www.WisdomoftheEarth.com

Cover illustration by Therese Desjardin
Cover design by Mark Short
Interior design by Blue Moon Publishing
www.SedonaBluemoon.com

Wisdom of the Earth Speaks

The Truth About Medicinal Aromatherapy

Barry B. Kapp

Table of Contents

Introduction

PART 1

The Truth About Medicinal Aromatherapy

PART 11

Frequently Asked Questions

PART III

Medicinal Angels

"And God said: 'Behold, I have given you
every herb yielding seed, which is upon the face of all
the earth, and every tree, in which is the fruit of a tree
yielding seed- to you it shall be for food: and to every
beast of the earth, and to every fowl of the air, and to
everything that creepeth upon the earth, wherein there
is a living soul, (I have given) every green herb for
food.' And it was so."

Genesis 1:29-30
(Torah,
According to the Masoretic Text)

"Look deep into nature
and then you will understand everything better"
-Albert Einstein

ACKNOWLEDGMENTS
and THANKSGIVING

I would like to say that without the following, I would not have completed this labor of love.

Thank you, CREATOR, for your constant love and vision to me.

Thank you, Tree and Plant Kingdom. for your belief in me, and your communication with me through the years.

Thank you, Dad, for the Wisdom Teaching that you gave me, from my earliest memory.

Thank you, Mom, for your heart-knowing to work with me and teach me how to communicate with the Trees and Plants.

Thank you, my twin ray, Cynthia, for your constant encouragement and prompting to please write my story. "The world should know what you have to tell them."

Thank you, all of my nine children, for the love, patience and guidance that you have given me on my path of life. You have taught me more than you will ever know.

Thank you, Joan K., for all of your support, which helped me to sustain my journey with Earth Mother through the years.

Thank you, Ellie O'Neill, for the amazing work in editing my book, which you so lovingly bestowed.

Thank you, Audre Wenzler, for your commitment to the Tree and Plant Kingdoms, and your faithfulness to Them to lead you on your journey. Your support is so grounding.

Thank you, all of my students, clients and patients, for all of your support, affirmations, and loyalty throughout the years.

Thank you so much my dear animal friends... birds, dogs, cats, cows, horses, sheep, goats, llamas, alpacas, deer, rabbits and all. You have shown me, over and over again how you love humans.

Thank you, friends, mentors, and teachers whom I have forgotten; I realized how important you are to me.

PREFACE
Believing Is One Strengh, Knowing Is Stronger

I would like to say at the beginning of this journey that I do not intend to use many references to validate my 'knowing' - my own particular term for the wisdom that I have accrued through communication with the Trees and Plants, by walking and talking with Them daily. Medicinal Aromatherapy is a daily lifestyle for me. I feel, experience and explore them daily. It is my only medicine. This book is for those who are already awakened in their hearts as to basic truths about the subject. The contents will resonate with many and put more of the pieces of the puzzle together for their own journey. There is a lot of information available explaining the points that I will speak about. But you may need to know the right places to find it.

This material is covered in the classes that are offered at **Wisdom of the Earth**, our school in Northern Arizona and many other locations in the U.S. However, it may be that the truths herein are self-evident, and that the 'heart-remembering' will take care of the rest with the guidance from those who have walked this path longer than you. Just know that walking with the Trees and Plants, having a relationship with Them, using Them as your medicine - physically, emotionally and spiritually is a lifestyle - a way of life.

One of my daughters told me that when she practices acting, she does not practice every now and then. No! Everyday she does something in the field she loves. She said, "Likewise Dad, Medicinal Aromatherapy is something you do every day."

I have worked with thousands of people over the years and I know what she is talking about. So many people have become disillusioned with so called traditional medicine, so when they come to me they were impressed with the results of the original medicine-aromatherapy. But only too soon, some of them went to drugs, and conventional treatments because the pressure to conform was too great, in one form or another, it knocks at their door. I have come to the conclusion that the attitude of superiority of humans, mixed with the teachings of giving one's power away to someone or something else, is very strong... so strong that many people do not rely on their own knowing and do not believe that they have the strength to carry through by themselves.

I would like to say another word about my heart's desire, regarding this book. I am a shaman of the Tree and Plant Kingdom. That means that I spend a good amount of time at Their feet, listening to Them, listening to their stories for me. The Trees and Plants remind me of many things that They can help to heal for both the human and animal kingdoms, and on all levels of dis-ease. It is such a blessing to remember that we can take back our power from those who have taught us falsely.

The Trees and Plants are the ones that we must seek help and advice from because we are incapable, unknowing, do not have the wisdom, and in this society- the rights by law- to take control of our own health physically, emotionally and spiritually. I regularly go out and sit down against a tree, put my arms around Her, or a bush shrub, etc., and just listen.

Chapter 7 of this book will explain how I do it. Also, I ceremonially hand pour the essences, listen and talk to the Trees and Plants at that time. Then I come back from that reality into the human reality and share what I have been told to anyone who is open to hear. My heart's desire is for you to know exactly what I am doing, why and what for. We are in the time of authenticity and integrity and that is the premise I am working under. The time is short and the best way to disclose shadow is to reveal light. The Mayan Calendar says this is the time we are living in, and we can see it happening all around us. It may be hard to accept but the time of secrets is over.

> *"You must teach your children that the ground beneath their feet is the ashes of our grandfathrs and grandmothers so that they will respect the land, tell your children that the earth is rich in the lives of our kin.*
>
> *Teach your children what we have taught our children - that the Earth is our Mother. Whatever befalls the Earth, befalls the sons and (daughters) of the Earth. When men (and women) spit upon the ground, they spit upon themselves.*
>
> *This we know. The Earth does not belong to man (or woman); man (and woman) belongs to the Earth. This we know. All things are connected like the blood, which unites one family. All things are connected.*
>
> *Whatever befalls the Earth, befalls the sons (and daughters) of the Earth. Man and (woman) did not weave the web of Life, they are merely a strand in it. Whatever they do to the web, they do it to themselves."*
>
> -Chief Seattle

Note To All Readers

This book represents the experiences, feelings and explorations of the author, Barry Kapp. He has the 'knowing' that taking 100% responsibility for his actions is the way of Peace, Joy and Divine Love. He also expects all who read his book to understand that, and hopefully, to live in the same spirit. The author does NOT take responsibility for other people's actions who read his book from a paradigm of Fear. That means reading his book, exploring something that is written in his book, then deciding to play the blame game and project 1 to 100% responsibility for his or her problems or hurts back on the author.

This book is an intimate sharing by the author and is shared by many. It is for any human that has an awakened consciousness and desires to come back to the Heart of the Mother for facilitation of healing physically, emotionally and spiritually. Any person who reads this and expects any medical experiences, suggestions or encouragements herein to be in compliance with only one health philosophy put forth by the Allopathic organizations and all their branches, should stop and take a deep breath and know that their expectations are old, outdated and wrong.

All they have to do is look around and do some study. They could go to Google and look under Alternative Medical Suggestions and they will see.

It is truly time to awake.

May all be blessed,

B.B. Kapp

INTRODUCTION

My Story

This story begins in 1949 with my earliest memories as a three-year-old in Northern Virginia. I remember feeling the excitement of my toes when stepping on, and squashing, the rotten apples that had fallen from a huge apple tree in my backyard. Those were days of cotton diapers only, completely natural in texture, and I loved them. My father had bought a pet Muscovy duck that became my best friend. I called him "Donald Duck". He loved to play tag with me, biting my calves whenever he caught me. I would scream, and my mother would come running. Yet no harm was ever done, just a growing bond and understanding of the ways of another species so loved by Creator.

I chose a mother and father who loved me dearly. The Earth and all its' species were near and dear to them, in the special enlightenment that they shared. Dad had a huge garden that, even then, was a bit uncommon in the suburbs of the nation's capital. My father was born in the Western city where gardens were common, and his father had a fresh vegetable and fruit market. Dad and mom taught me explicitly that, "to love Creator is to love Earth Mother, and to love Earth Mother is to love Creator." Dad would let me play in the fresh cultivated furrows of our garden, not worrying a bit about any harm coming to me. Again, I was only in my diapers. Generally cold weather wasn't a problem in the late summer, but colder weather brought a few more clothes! The dirt felt soft, warm and inviting in my mouth... and the dirt *would* disappear. Dad saw me eating dirt, stopped the tractor, and said, "Eating dirt will build your immune system and keep you from getting every little sickness." Years later, he reminded me of that and added, "With herbs and essences, tasting is equally as important as smelling. If you do enough, your body will remember what you are smelling, and help inform you if it is pure or not."

He taught me to always eat the core of an apple, the rind of a lemon or lime, and never to peel a potato or sweet potato, because these parts of vegetables are good. My dad was not a vegetarian or vegan but he did not eat pork or red meat. This caused more than one argument between dad and mom. Dad would say, "The do's always outweigh the don'ts, but common sense, knowledge and wisdom are priceless." Staying connected with Mother Earth is the major gateway to true knowledge, true intelligence and true wisdom. My father speaks loudly through me today. Dishonoring our ancestors, in any way, will only bring disaster because these remembrances are paramount to staying grounded and surviving as a species. Honoring our elders enables us to move forward to new dimensions of consciousness.

Mom had dozens of rose bushes that she nurtured as if they were her children. I had three siblings, one was five years older than me, and the other two were 10-14 years younger than me. Mother was a farm girl of nine siblings, she being the youngest. When my grandmother was carrying my mother, lightening struck the front porch that she was standing on. Out of the fear, and the energy, which burst from the bolt of lightening, Grandma Elizabeth was thrown forward, catching herself with both hands on her right leg to brace herself. This experience never left her, and when my mother was born she had a birthmark on her right leg. Grandma would comment that my mother was going to be special carrying a message of most importance respecting the Creator. Mom never spoke much about it. Her desire to teach me was powerful.

Around the age of eight, I had become the question-box son to mom and dad. At times I would exhaust them with so many questions. At different times while working with mom in her flower garden, I would ask her if people could talk to flowers... and would they speak back? Her favorite plants were roses, and it was through them that she taught me how to talk and listen to Them for answers. And you know what? It worked. One day my mother was deadheading her roses and she had me helping, by her side. She looked at me and said, "Son, did you know that you can ask this rose bush a question and tomorrow when we come out to work again the rose will answer you. I don't remember what I had asked that rose bush, which had such beautiful flowers that smelled so enchanting. I do know that I did get an answer. When I told my mother that an answer had come, she looked me straight in the eye, with her hands grasped firmly on each shoulder and said, "Believe your answer and never doubt it." How thankful I am for those ever resounding words from my precious mother for my journey ahead.

I would like to tell you about my own experiences, both personal and private at that early time in my life. Along with the questions galore that I had about everything, I asked my mom even more pressing questions. I asked about the universe, such as: Where did I come from; were there other people like us on other planets like Earth? My mother was always kind and would answer in an encouraging way; but in my heart of hearts I knew that I was from somewhere else. I was here for a reason, and I was going to find out what that reason was as soon as I could. It would take years, but my determination was great.

I now know that where I came from, before coming to Earth Mother, is from among the planets in our solar system. Why is this also important for you to know? Deny it or not, all of our roots and bloodlines are important. Also many of you who will read this book already know me and desire me to authenticate my story so that others may profit from what I have to say, no matter whether people desire to hear the truth or not. I ask you to realize that there is so much more for you, the reader, to know about our Earth Mother. More than what you have been (most likely) programmed to believe through politics, culture or religion. What truly matters is that any amount of separation from all of the species on this planet, which are truly still in harmony with Creator, only means a most isolated existence- full of loneliness, fear and a downward spiral from Light Consciousness, and Divine Love. Please remember that!

To repeat again what I had said earlier, "True remembrance, true knowledge, true intelligence, and true wisdom come from living in harmony with Earth Mother and all other species on this planet." We have been loaned our bodies via Mother Earth to walk our journey here in love and gladness, bonding, fellowship, working together with *all* other species here as equals, and not superior to any.

Now let's continue my story further. When I was 11 and in the fourth grade, I had a wonderful math teacher who would always tell my class that, "Repetition is the Mother of Learning". I am forever thankful for her most gracious truthful words. It helped me have courage down thru life as I saw circumstances repeat themselves over and over again until I would really, "get it", and then move on to the next lesson.

Around the age of 12-14, I realized just how many dreams I had on a regular basis. I talked to my Mom about this and she advised me to be still at the end of the dream, and ask my heart for guidance. She also told me to ask my angels to help me understand if any of my dreams were important to remember. I did just that and learned many things from my dreams. Also, around this same time, there would be times when I would feel really bad that something painful is happening to someone somewhere and I did not know what to do with the feelings. It finally "got to me", so much that again, I talked to my Mother about these painful experiences that I was having. I asked her if there was anyone in the family that was ill or that might be dying? Most of the time she would say, "No, not that she was aware of."

Finally, one morning as I was preparing for school, my Mother caught eye of me and asked me if I was feeling those pains and sorrowful feelings again? I responded, "Yes" and said, "What am I suppose to do with these experiences"? She then responded and told me that I was destined at an early age to feel the pangs of sorrow from Mother Earth, and what she was experiencing from human abuse. She told me that I was also experiencing sorrows of humans from long distances where there was an accident of some kind, etc. Mom then encouraged me to feel the feelings, and then give all of that energy back to God, for it was not for me to keep holding on to after I felt the feelings deep enough. Mom said that these experiences would help me for my journey ahead, and that I must not hold on to them too long or they will make me literally physically sick. What grand advice my dear Mother gave me. My Mom and I were inseparable.

When I was fifteen, Dad and Mom took another trip West to see his Mom, brothers and half sister. This was the fifth trip, so I was really looking forward to it. My older sister and I were always excited about these 'going west' trips. We were in a really nice 1956 Dodge four-door sedan and Dad had it all fixed up for camping. We camped several nights in Bryce Canyon, Utah, and I just loved it there. I felt God so close to me, but the best part was that I got to spend time with my Dad on an intimate level. We were returning from a long hike, just Dad and me. We had been talking about a lot of things concerning life, his knowing, and desires for his only son at that time.

We stopped to rest and as we sat on a rock outcropping, sipping on water he begin to speak words that would influence and shape me from hence forward. "You know son Barry, I prayed a long time that God would give me a son. He answered me and you, Barry are the son I was given. I had told Creator that if a son was given to me, at the proper time, I would from my heart release him back to Him. Dad told me that he had been trying to teach me, from his heart, all truths that had been handed down to him by his parents and grand parents, as well as from his own experiences, explorations and feelings. The time had come to begin to release me back. He thanked me for being such a good son and he saw Creator working in my life." I shed tears in my own private way for days after that discussion on the trail. Dad and I had bonded for life. Now Mom and Dad and me were a solid cord not easily broken.

By the age of 19, I was enrolled in a college in the Midwest. The year was 1965 and I was very proactive in the hippie generation. I was anti-establishment in many areas, and very interested in spiritual truths and masters who truly walked the talk. I was bored in school and chose to join a seafarer's union, to be taught how to become a seaman. My heart aim was to get the job and then when ashore in the foreign country of my choosing, I would leave and look for truth in other lands. I never actually completed that ambition because I felt my heart and spiritual guides saying 'no'. "Stay here, there are experiences for you here that you should feel and go through for your journey ahead." Then I decided to join the Peace Corps and got accepted to South Central India for 2 years.

The Vietnam War was raging also at this very time and I was totally opposed to it. I was opposed to violence, period, of any kind. At the same time, I fell in love and got married. So many experiences were going on at the same time, and my heart was becoming overwhelmed. I was happy and content. My wife also applied for the Peace Corps and got accepted. The only problem was that they did not have enough room for both of us at the same place. We said, we are not doing that, so we both went back to college where we had met. At that very time, my draft board changed my classification to 1A, which meant that I was to be inducted immediately.

I did not believe, as I said, in violence of any kind, so I refused. I had other friends who had gone to other countries and invited us to stay with them. We actually traveled out of the country, twice, before I knew that it was my choice to stay and face 'whatever' for my journey ahead. Well, after more than a year, the FBI found me. Finally, I found myself in front of a judge with chains around my wrists and dangling down to my ankles. This dialogue started; the officer comes in and announced my case, "The United States of America against Barry Kapp". "Stand up, come forward to the judge and remain standing." I did just that and the judge and I were looking into each other's eyes face-to-face. The judge looked down at my files, then looked up at me and started to talk. "So I see here that according you your statements, your God is not made with hands?" I replied, 'No, never was, isn't and never will be, your honor'. In other words, my loyalty to my Creator was higher and over ruled any mandate my man could proclaim. I then proceeded to tell him gently but firmly the following, "I do not believe any human being ever has the right to tell another human being to take up weapons and put himself or herself or another in harms' way." He then got so angry with me that he immediately took his gavel and slammed it down so hard on his bench that I thought it might break. He commenced to say, 'You are one of the most despicable human beings that I have ever met and I am going to sentence you to one year in the federal penitentiary. Now get out of my sight for I am going to make citizens out of several persons desiring to be a part of this great country. I am going to tell them that this country was brought by blood and it will take blood to keep it that way. I hope you think about this long and hard while in prison.' This was a life-changing moment in my life. Why? Because I knew as never before that I had done the right thing. Though very hard, my experience in prison was one of the most profound of my life. It definitely prepared me for who I am now. My book definitely reflects this part of my journey. I am speaking about learning about Fear versus Love, and strength to walk it.

During this same time period, I had another huge awakening that I must share. Marriage was precious to me, which also meant the possibility of little creations springing from the loins of me and the womb of my wife. We had discussed childbirth a lot and felt that we did not desire to go with the traditional modern way of hospitals and the like. Childbirth was a beautiful ceremony to us that should take place in the sanctity of our home if at all possible. So, we studied books on natural childbirth and prepared ourselves.

In 1968, my wife birthed our first child, with me by her side, delivering the baby, surrounded by the presence of our guardian angels and spirit guides. This experience was going to happen to me 9 times. It was so amazing to witness a birth of new life. Our first son came from the world of the womb and I held his head as he began to come into this world. He was quiet until just at the right moment and then I saw two wondrous movements simultaneously happening before my eyes. An angel at my left was blowing the 'wind breath of life' into our little son's mouth and my son inhaled a great big breath. Then came the big exhale with a beautiful new birth cry from my son. I will never forget those miracle moments of birth and the working together of 3 dimensions all at the same time. This is where my first realization came, that Mother Earth teaches each one of us when we first enter this dimension. **It is truly more blessed to receive than to give!** It is only through receiving in a surrendered and vulnerable place, that we can then truly understand how to give. Without an inhale, there is no exhale. We as humans have twisted this truth 180 degrees and it is time to return.

These simple experiences can give us the knowing about life as it really is. And then, one more story about childbirth that I would like to mention here, and one that has given me new insight, although, it was both excruciating and joyous at the same time. Our third child, second daughter, was due any day. I was working at a hardware store and got a call that I should come home immediately because the baby was coming. I got home quickly and within a few hours realized that something was wrong - unlike the other two births. My wife and I prayed, relaxed into the breathing and then she began to push. As the past experiences had prepared me, I proceeded as before until the crowning started, and I saw my precious little daughter had the umbilical cord wrapped around her neck and her color was becoming blue. I took a deep inhale and asked for guidance from all my spirit helpers. I did not tell my wife at first for fear of scaring her. Then a most amazing phenomenon happened. My hands started to move without my own exertion of energy. I immediately heard a voice that told me to just let my guide do the work, using my hands. Our little girl's body moved this way and that way until the cord became loose and I was able to take the cord gently off from around her neck. Her face returned to beautiful pinkish red color and then I started crying for joy. I then told her mother what had happened and we said a thanksgiving blessing about the whole event. The placenta came naturally in good time as the previous two births. It was our custom and ceremony to bury the placenta in our garden- thanking Creator and Mother Earth for the blessing of new life. This experience taught me many things, but especially how to own my trust that these spiritual helpers, guides, angels are really there for us, if we but ask and then let them teach us. I have many more stories that have helped shape and groom me for my journey with the Tree and Plant Kingdom but may this suffice for this book.

May this book resonate with you, is my earnest desire. I can assure you my words will ring true with your heart. Why? Because my words, though expressed differently, here or there, say the same truth as has been passed down from the beginning. These words are *Mitakuye Oyasin* - All things are connected and Light and Divine Love are all there really is. Bearing this in mind, we can go forward on a little journey into the great and beautiful world of Medicinal Aromatherapy. It will branch out from the center like spokes on a wheel. The center being Medicinal Aromatherapy, and then, the twelve spokes, all distinct topics, but all intimately and ultimately interconnected.

May you be blessed!

MA = Medicinal Aromatherapy
HH = Heart of the Heavens
HE = Heart of the Earth
HOOH = Heart of our Heart
HOC = Heart of the Creator
E, S, W, N, = The Four Directions

The cover diagram is the culmination of a dream that I had in regards to being called to write this book. Medicinal Aromatherapy is at the center like the hub of a wheel. The spokes span out into 12 points that cover all the areas that Medicinal Aromatherapy encompasses on this Earth Mother. The Star of David represents the male energy in each one of us and the cirlce aound the Star of David represents the female energy in each one of us. The four directions represents the honoring of every part of Earth Mother. Then there is the 4 Heart Points that are vital to our understanding Truth and walking on each of our journeys here on this dimension. The colors point to the rainbow that has such beautiful distinct shades yet all working in concert with each other.

Blessings to you on your exciting pathway,
B.B. Kapp

My Prayer For All Who Enter Herein. . .

I now call forth the heart of the Heavens, the heart of the Earth, the heart of the Trees and Plants to speak to each one who reads further, to guide, protect and give heart understanding. What you have been looking for, you will find it within the heart of the Tree and Plant Kingdoms. They are Wisdom Teachers. They are grounding Pillars in these times of extraordinary changes. May you, my dear readers, receive these thoughts with love. Divine Creator and Spirit, El Shaddai, enlighten all who enter these pages with their heart of hearts. I ask You, to give them what they are looking for. Give them memories, give them understanding, and give them help. So be it...

-B.B.Kapp

PART 1

THE TRUTH ABOUT MEDICINAL AROMATHERAPY

CHAPTER ONE

Medicinal Aromatherapy
Is The
Original Medicine
Of The Planet

*"The art of Healing comes from nature,
not from the physician.
Therefore the physician must start from
nature, with an open mind."*
-Paracelus

Let's talk for a moment about our ancient cultures and their effect on modern life. Down through the ages, humans have had two dominant ways of thinking, believing, and therefore, manifesting. One way is represented by cultures that base their society on *concepts* and *percepts*, and the other is represented by cultures based on *precepts*. What is the difference between the two?

Conception and Perception

conception: *ancient oral tradition cultures that felt and intuited the way to live on Mother in Harmony. They walked and lived from their inner heart where no duality exists.*

perception: *ancient oral tradition cultures that saw how other species follow each other in Harmony on Mother and did the same trusting, loving, and walking their journey of life here.*

preception: *laws upon laws created by humans who desired to rule over one another in this or that way. Precept cultures ultimately sprung from fear-based humans that saw no benefit in trusting the loving tenets of Earth Mother just as She is, Intact and Whole.*

Conception and perception in cultures with strong 'oral traditions' involve working and living in harmony with divine love and guidance. Traditional peoples seek to understand the tenets and ways of Earth Mother. The elders- both women and men- hold on to loving the Creator with all their hearts and souls. At one time, their ancestors walked and talked with all species. Concept and percept cultures keep this knowledge in their hearts, and hand it down from generation to generation.

The guidelines of the Mother are much different than 'human

precepts'.[1] To love Creator with all your heart, soul, and mind and to love your neighbor as yourself-this is the self-knowing principle borne in everyone's heart. These tenets are not unique to just one belief system, but traditional (oral) cultures have handed these same tenets down from the beginning of time. Judaism, Christianity, Islam, and many polytheistic religions do not have the original, true knowledge from the Source. Their claims of entitlement are empty as to on how happiness, peace and joy truly flow here on Earth Mother.

As an example, at one time, Judaism was a religion of oral traditions with its own set of percepts and concepts. The first 300 years of Christianity were the same. Then something changed. Culture shifted its course, relying on precepts rather than direct experience of the divine. The confusion that ensued from this change in direction and the resulting judgment lying in the core semantics of monotheistic believers, brought a wave of dogmatic decrees that effectively wiped out many of the traditional societies in the Middle East, Europe and Great Britain. The elders were driven from their temples, killed and the teaching scattered and became hidden in remote places when the long arm of Rome could not find them. The oral traditions continued to be passed down in secret. This pattern of history has been repeated over and over.

Monotheists say that 'God' is just 'one' Being and they are at odds with the polytheistics who hold that there are many "Gods." I will tell you point blank that in my few short years on this planet, these are all stupid ploys and a ridiculous waste of words, because both groups of humans ultimately believe that there is ONE ULTIMATE CREATOR with the unity of both female and male vibrations ABOVE ALL, PERIOD.

Whether you believe that Jesus is God, or that the Gods of Eastern religions are the true expression of the Creator, these are just expressions of purely human tenets- ones that separate us from each other and Source. Despite this intellectual seperation, the CREATOR IS VERY MUCH INTACT WITHIN ALL OF OUR HEARTS. Whether we act upon it- that is another question.

Creator is just so wonderfully above and beyond all the stuff that is wrapped up in man-made tenets of politics, religion, etc. Yet, Creator is present in simple spirituality of the cultures based on conception[2] and perception[3]. The wisdom of oral tradition cultures is passed on year-after-year, generation-after-generation, and has proven to be more accurate and preserving than the precepts cultures whose laws do not pass the test of time. Precept cultures create laws upon laws, which do not acknowledge basic divine principles. **They plant their tenets with feet heading in two different directions creating polarities, and inevitably, digressing into their own self-serving agendas**. The Creator is forgotten, and the tried and experienced journeys of the ancient masters are tossed to the side. Endless written pages, trillions of them, spiral down, only to get trapped in their own contradictions. They cause a deadening effect on life. Precept cultures have taken their own contrived way. It's not the way of all the other species on this planet and its causing irreparable harm to the planet. Living in harmony, staying close to Mother Earth, listening to Her and acknowledging Her from the heart is the *only* way to joy, happiness and balance.

Medicinal Aromatherapy is the *original medicine* of the planet. Common sense teaches this. Remember that herbs and essences are exactly what our ancient ancestors have always used, because they are part of the divine plan from the beginning. Oral traditions help us to understand that the Trees and Plants were here *before* our species. Our ancestors knew about the medicine from the Trees and Plants because their oral tradition told them so. Creator made a special covenant with the Trees and Plants.

This covenant revealed that They are here as a major catalyst for the four basic building blocks of life: carbon, hydrogen, oxygen and nitrogen. Trees and Plants also facilitate our healing -spiritually, emotionally, and physically. One of my mentors, Zachariah Sitchin, in his writings, the *Earth Chronicles*, indicates that the ancient Sumerian civilization was developed from the teachings of special and highly developed mentors. The Sumerians were taught many secrets by the Annunaki, from the planet Nibiru. In the beginning, *all* life here on earth was actually seeded from other planets. This was a special gift for Earth Mother.

But let's go a little deeper before we talk solely about medicinal aromatherapy. By now, you realize that I put much more credibility in oral traditions than written ones. Why? I will tell you again, but in a different way.

Have you ever noticed how the anthropologists or archeologists make it appear that the further back you go in human history, the dumber the human species appears! Humanity had no written language as we understand written language, therefore, they are considered dumb. But no, no, no! The truth is that cultures of the oral tradition saw no value in many of the things we idolize today. Understand that most ancient cultures *chose* oral traditions. They knew that inherent within these traditions was the foundational understanding of the 'vibratory energy transfer'. Think of all the masters that taught their intimate disciples with only the human word and not the written word. Disciples had the advantage of the words of the master and his or her direct vibratory energies- both at the same time! This way was priority for them and their symbol writing was secondary, yet valuable. Their way was not to leave huge amounts of written texts for the future generations to misinterpret. They desired to blend with all of the species of the earth, work from the heart... and do amazing things via the heart energies. They communicated in ways that we are just remembering now.

Two of my teachers, Jose Arguelles and Drunvalo Melchizedek teach all over the world. They remind us that the time will come when the technologies that we have created will be returned to within our bodies.[5] We will once again be able, as in times of old, to telepathically work with one another without all of the outside communication apparatus like ipods, cell phones, computers, etc. We will even transport ourselves without the use of outside vehicles, and so forth...

Today there are still a few cultures that live this way in remote regions. Like our ancient ancestors, they choose to live in harmony with Earth Mother. They are content. This contentment comes from remembering all of the magical possibilities and realities of our true power. Power, based on divine love and oneness with the whole universe, will propel us to higher levels of consciousness. These higher dimensions and octaves of consciousness will reunite us with our friends, relatives and ancestors that are beyond this wonderful planet called Earth.

Our ancestors, who chose the concept and percept way, came into this world to experience earth life, and then moved on to their next experience in spirit and body. They quickly completed their mission here, staying close to Earth Mother without having to digress so wildly into the cultures of precepts. They were the cultures of laws upon laws with everything written down. The arrogant superiority of these laws has created great 'straying behaviors' of all kinds, spiraling us down, away from Light, true remembrance, true knowledge, true intelligence and true wisdom. The fall from grace was a short distance, but life- changing. We went from living in the heart to living in the mind.

I find it so interesting that in our culture, a great culture of precepts, that we run around like the anthropologists and archeologists saying that we are more evolved than traditional cultures. Really, we are the ones that do not understand, and are quite retarded!

Today, in 2008, many of us are awakening to the prophecies about the changes happening all around us. We are drinking them in, and realizing that even our written prophecies are outdated when compared to the accuracy of what the oral traditions have been saying all along.

The Trees and Plants have been here all along; loving us, giving us all beautiful things, giving us Their essences for spiritual, emotional and physical harmony. We call this healing. Their DNA is so similar to ours. Much has been written about this, so do a Google search, if you desire to know more.

In the last 150 years or so humans, our species, have embarked on a path, which has increasingly separated itself from its roots. Pharmaceutical medicine has evolved and created the monsters of artificially-created drugs. Sadly, these drugs cannot be produced without side effects. I am speaking about products of the allopathic philosophy of health and wellbeing, which advocates the notions that: When in doubt, cut it out,and the treating of symptoms, instead of preventive medicine. It's easier to create drugs for humans instead of really working with a loving heart to correct the dis-ease. Greed, profit, power, control over humans are the mainstay of allopathic medicine, while true and pure healing brings results of wellness spiritually, emotionally and physically.

The use of Tree and Plant medicine, the original medicine is the pathway to true healing. Thank the Creator that more and more individuals are awakening!

Did you know that when the Sumerian tablets of Nineveh were decoded, they spoke of the Annunaki as teaching two great secrets to our physical ancestors? One was the secret of water, and the other, the secret of essential essences. Many erroneously use the term essential *oils*, which I understand through study, and mostly through what the Trees and Plants directly tell me, has been mistranslated from older languages. The word 'oils' has been substituted for 'essences'. This has altered the meaning. Oils denote greasiness, whereas pure essences are not greasy. This description pertains to nut oils such as almond, rose hip, etc. I have endeavored in my teachings to refer to the *quintessence* of a Tree or Plant as an essence, and not oil. It can ultimately be very confusing.

In my teaching, I also often refer to herbs and essences together. You may be wondering about this. Over the years, my remembrance and teaching came mainly from the Trees and Plants. This is the true medicinal aromatherapy via essential essences. Knowledge of these secret teachings can be found throughout history and are made available to serious and devoted healers.

There came times when certain individuals have remembered the great power of pure essential essences, and that they knew that They could be used to translate to other levels, dimensions and octaves of consciousness. These special healers desired to wait until Earth Mother evolved, as they no longer desired to remain and live with the dense *shadow* that reigned here. Some of our ancestors, at this point, became very fearful of the power of essential essences and they chose to use the less powerful fresh, or dried herbs, for their medicines. It wasn't that they did not recognize the beauty in the essences, but there was a difference of opinion as to how and when they should be used medicinally. This was a decision about whether to stay, or not, on this dimension. The difference in opinion was over love versus fear. Down through the ages, the Wisdom and Knowledge of the power of the essences went underground and they were taught in many Mystery Schools.

Reflections

There is a beautiful essential essence called Betula lenta, (Birch, sweet or black). This essence is hard to find, not because there are few Birch sweet Trees but because there are so few farmers distilling it. Today, however there is alot of Birch essence on the market and where do you suppose it comes from? The laboratory companies that synthetically make it. It is so sad. What is more sad is that many people in our country who are into the aromatherapy world on some level cannot tell the difference. The reason is simple. They do not know what real Birch smells like and they take no responsibility to search it out. Also, their disconnection with Earth Mother is so acute, that it is too late for many of them to worry about such because their lives are so full of disharmony, why bother? Even in our day of specialist's who claim they trust the system of science, the induction and deduction postulate, there are huge problems. They have been taught in our educational system that pure science is concerned with learning new facts only for the sake of gaining new knowledge. Applied science is the practical use of scientific theory and laws. What about Wisdom which is the ability to know how to use the knowledge that we learn? Well, I know a scientist who is a wonderful aromatherapist, yet was deceived about Birch from labs and true Birch. Unless we go deeper into Earth Mother and the Tree and Plant kingdom, this is what can happen. The scientist felt bad about being mistaken and made it know. Blessed is that human who calls a spade a spade when the truth is brought forward. The fear paradigm is truly fearful of what love is accomplishing today, and they who walk in the fear path will do anything to copy, mimic or imitate that which is truly natural. They strive to neutralize the power of the love paradigm in any and every way that they can. Believe me, they do quite a job, especially after so many people have been dumbed down. But guess what, they will never succeed with those of us who choose the love paradigm. Why? Because ALL things that are pure and natural have a vibratory frequency that humans cannot precisely duplicate in any way, shape or form. Try as they will, it maddens them to no end that this cannot be accomplished. So they take other routes of action as we have discussed to steal our souls. Be aware but walk in the paradigm of love and you will be free.

---

(1) The cultures based on precepts started a long time ago, but in ancient times were still the exception, and not the rule here on this planet. Precepts means laws upon laws created by humans who desired to rule over one another in this or that way. Precept cultures ultimately sprung from fear-based humans that saw no benefit in trusting the loving tenets of Earth Mother just as She is, Intact and Whole.

(2) Conception here means ancient oral tradition cultures that felt and intuited the way to live on Mother in Harmony. They walked and lived from their inner heart where no duality exists.

(3) Perception means ancient oral tradition cultures that saw how other species follow each other in Harmony on Mother and did the same trusting, loving, walking their journey of life here.

(4) The way of concepts and percepts

(5) That we touch and handle

CHAPTER TWO

Medicinal Aromatherapy Is Based On Pure Love – Not Fear

"It is at the edge of a petal that love waits."

-William Carlos Williams

It might seem strange at first that this is part of my book, but it is the foundation to what the Trees and Plants are all about. Let me tell you, They work from a paradigm of Divine Love, not fear. They feel joy, love, pain, sorrow, desire for rain or sunshine, but do not respond to control, fear, hate, malice, jealousy, violence or an unforgiving nature. And since They bask in this paradigm of Divine Love, They are powerful when they are pure and not diluted with a carrier oil and other substances. Many aromatherapy authors write constantly about not using undiluted essences 'neat" because of fear. These authors perpetuate the paradigm of fear - not love. I do not dilute pure, medicinal-grade essences and They tell me not to, for reasons that I will mention later on in this book. Many of these same aromatherapy authors are afraid to say what they do in their real lives for fear of legal action. Also these authors may be 'aromatherapists', just in it for the money, because of its recent popularity as a fad, and not practicing the healing art of true medicinal aromatherapy. Or, it could be that they have only been taught something based on fear... and they have never questioned the concept at all.

There are many so-called reasons for all the lies that hold no credibility. I can tell you two stories from direct experience to further help you understand.

A few years back, I was at a symposium that was attended by medicinal aromatherapists from all over the country. There was a woman speaker talking about how she treated a certain condition with specific essences. She proceeded to tell the audience how she would dilute the essence with a 'carrier' oil. After her talk she opened it up for Q & A. Someone then asked the question if she had treated the same problem on herself, would she have diluted the essences? She said, "no," however, due to her fear of lawsuits, she advised her client differently. This caused a great discussion amongst over 500 people. I spoke with others, asking, "When are we going to live in our integrity, and stop worrying about the fear paradigm?" "How are our dear fellow brothers and sisters, who are new at this, ever going to know the truth if we do one thing and tell them to do something else." Someone even mentioned that it may be okay to not tell clients the truth, because they were not likely to use pure essences. Not a correct answer! Tell your client to only use pure essences and to use them 'neat' if they truly desire results and to also avoid potential problems.

I have also noted that someone on a web page mentioned that essences are stronger when you dilute them. Wrong! Untrue! Why doesn't that person go get a good bottle of wine, dilute it, and then give it to their friends and ask them if they like it better? I must tell you, dear ones, that there are a lot of fear-based lies, well- meaning or not, that should be brought out into the open. I believe, many times it is just a by-product of what the fear-based medical institutions have done to us. We try our wings in alternative medicine and bring most of the baggage of fear right into it.

Reflections

There is another story from one of my classes, several years ago. A student who had been taught via left-brained, fear-based, medicinal aromatherapy decided that the essences were not really working for her, and she desired to be taught by a right-brained aromatherapist/shaman that came from a paradigm of love and not fear. She came to class having been taught by some of the best-known aromatherapy teachers in the world... so there was some resistance in her heart even though her guides told her to come. The first day I spoke about using pure essences 'neat' on the largest organ of the body, the skin. (It should be done topically for the best results with the essences.) We passed around the essences and I saw her reluctance, yet she went ahead as she saw her classmates responding freely. She felt no danger, and there were no bad side effects, either. That night she wrestled with what she had been taught previous to this class.

She had never doubted or questioned her instruction, and never tried to use pure essences 'neat' on her skin. Then she realized that she had been taught wrong. The experiences of the day before empowered her like never before. She knew that she had been rightly guided to our class. The whole class encouraged her, so she awakened to the sad fact of what has gone on for far too long. Why had this happened? Do you really desire that I teach you, or can you figure out or intuit, the major reason why?

Many of the old authors, since the revival of aromatherapy in the 1960's, came from the UK. They were well programmed to let the allopathic profession deal with their idea of "real medical problems", but the aromatherapists could use diluted essences for the good smells and a litle emotional uplift. Again, what I found is that aromatherapists from both camps, were, and still are, giving away their power to the same old precepts. This power give-away puts human superiority at the highest level of credibility.

They do not TRUST EARTH MOTHER. They do not see the link and bridge that Creator has with Earth Mother, yet they talk about God so much, and create man-made statutes that have nothing to do with God. Yet truthfully, as my Mother and Father taught me, "to know God is to know and harmonize with Mother Earth and all species that reside on, in and above Her. And to know Her and live in peace, love and harmony with Her and all other species is to know God." And to speak plainly, the abyss gets deeper and deeper as you search it out. Folks, it is a waste of time at this stage of the game to speak more on this. **Just know that when you choose pure essences out of a heart of divine love, you will mirror Their power and potential, which in turn will bless you with not only correcting disease, but also maintaining your immunity in these times of great anxiety and stress.**

CHAPTER THREE

Medicinal Aromatherapy Brings Harmony and Peace

"Ever viewed a field of WHEAT, OATS OR BARLEY waving in the wind, with the SUN shining? PEACE and HARMONY will never be seen clearer."

-B.B. Kapp

DIVINE LOVE is the strongest force in all existence. I believe most of us know and remember this from our heart core. Divine Love is what motivates Earth Mother as She awakens and cleanses Herself, and evolves to the next dimension of Her consciousness between now and 2012-2013. Some of our human brothers and sisters, who are here at this time, still remember high spiritual truths of what it was like to have permission to come to Earth as a spirit, entering a human embryo or walking in at a later time, with permission. They say that there is a female Stargate that we all go through to enter Earth Mother. Some of us remember- some do not. Anyway, the female Stargate requires a remembrance of the following, which must be heart uttered in order to have permission to go through. It goes like this. Love and Truth create Beauty, Beauty creates Trust, Trust creates HARMONY and PEACE, and HARMONY and PEACE create Respect for the Great Creator.

So true, indeed!

When we permit the Tree and Plant Kingdom to enter our lives knowingly and willingly, we open the door for Their permission to bless us with harmony and peace. This is Their every day experience on this beautiful planet. They live here too and are just as concerned as you and I are about what is going on. Tapping into Their life force and source by using pure essences opens doors of possibilities of renewed energy, new paradigms of thinking from Their perspectives and not just the human.

Living in Sedona, we see a lot of people seeking their life's purpose and they come to study with many teachers who either live here or are passing through for a brief seminar or workshop. But, I have noticed in the last several years that there are individuals coming to Sedona not to be taught by humans, but by other species such as rocks, animals, birds and yes...

Tree and Plants

Three years ago the Trees and Plants spoke to me very strongly, telling me that I should start telling my students that it is time to start remembering the benefit of sitting at the feet of a Tree and letting "US" teach you about what They know. Harmony and Peace are two such concepts that They are adept in. They feel and experience it every moment. They give themselves to us in the form of essential essences and we experience Their very life force in our blood stream. We become blood relatives to Them once again. They love us so much. The ancients say we are the children of the Trees and Plants; without Them we cannot survive, not only physically, but also emotionally and spiritually. Our ancestors were taught by the Trees and Plants from Aleph to Tau, from beginning to end.

So if you are struggling with anxiety, and fear in your life, experience pure **Laurel Leaf** *(Laurus noblis)* over your heart (about 10 drops for an adult), before you shower, and feel and experience Her power within your emotional life. She will speak to you. You may not know how to listen at first, but you will if you are walking with your heart first. Remember, your heart will never demean, violate or insult your mind. Your heart will use your heart mind and your brain mind appropriately. However, we have been taught the opposite. Your mind will and can lie, and demean your heart, hence, a basic reason for the problems we see around us. Harmony and Peace are what most of the human species truly desire. But, there is plenty of indigenous prophetic evidence, and direct contact from our relatives in other star systems, that those who do not desire Harmony and Peace will leave Earth Mother and go back to locations that they are more comfortable in. Remember, Harmony and Peace abide with us after Love, Truth, Beauty and Trust reside in our hearts. Pure essential essences are great Teachers of these very attributes that we are seeking. They will bring us to the door of remembrance but will never do the work for us. That work is for us to do. We must take 100% responsibility for our actions and do the work in our own individual lives so that we can flow with the changes that are happening now here on Earth Mother.

Reflections

In March 2004, our 2 year-old prized Shire stallion, Major, fell mysteriously ill. He was rushed to the closest veterinarian hospital, where he spent 13 days undergoing chest taps, blood test, and substantial lab work, all attempting to diagnose his illness. The vet essentially fire-hosed him with antibiotics, changing the type of antibiotic 4 different times. This led to laminitus (where the hoof wall begins to separate from the underlying tissue, similar to chemotherapy patients losing their fingernails), and blindness.

I had taken a A Medical Aromatherapy course from Kurt Schnaubelt Ph.D., and as I was medically and ethically opposed to the treatment the vet was giving Major, I contacted him for some help. He refereed me to Barry. Understanding Major's symptoms, Barry put together a package designed specifically for Major. Fed Ex got it to me two days later (we're on the big Island of Hawaii, and there is no such thing as overnight service). When the oils arrived, Major was standing in the corner of his stall, head almost touching the ground, with blood dripping out of both nostrils. He would not eat or drink anything. and showed profound lethargy. basically, he had given up , and so had the vet. She had been "preparing" us for the worst from the second day he was at the vet hospital, telling us we'd probably have to put him down.

I applied large quantities of oils to Major in rectal suppositories and on acupuncture points all over his body. At Barry's suggestion, I paid particular attention to lifting his spirits using the essential essence of rose. He showed an almost immediate response to the essences, and began to eat and drink a little.

After two days, we decided to take him home (against the vet's recommendation), where we continued to apply essential essences on Major. He showed continue improvement, and is now completely normal, except for the blindness that several much more experienced vets have attributed to the regiment of multiple antibiotics, rather than his illness.

I feel strongly that if these symptoms ever appear again in Major or in any other of our herd of registered Shires, we will treat at home with essential essences, and not even consider taking the horse to the vet.

Mahalo nui loa (usually translated from Hawaiian as "thank you very much", but really it's much more beautiful than that: *"Mahalo"* means Thank you, *"nui"* means great, and *"loa"* means everlasting or forever. So the real translation is more like

"Great thanks, everlasting" to Barry for his help in bringing our beloved stallion home. Thank you S. Friend for your faith in the Trees and Plants with Their beautiful medicine.

CHAPTER FOUR

Medicinal Aromatherapy Versus The Superiority Problem Of Our Species

"If Seeds in the black earth can turn into
such beautiful Roses, what might not the Heart of
Man become in its long journey toward the Stars?"

-G.K.Chesteron

"What a desolate place would be a world without a Flower! It would be a face without a smile, a feast without a welcome. Are not Flowers the Stars of the earth, and are not our Stars the Flowers of the Heaven."

-A. J. Balfour

"Joy is a net of Love by which you catch souls."

-Francis Quarles

This is not an easy topic, my dear ones. It is probably the most denied subject amongst us. There are so many levels of superiority that we are steeped in. There is a great spider web of illusion and deception. And guess what? It plays right into the hands of the shadow governments, those that desire to rule, control and keep us as zombies. Yes, they are feeling their superiority over us, but that is their way, and hopefully not ours.

Right from the start, I would like to mention something that is integral for those of us that have been programmed directly or indirectly by monotheistic beliefs. In the Torah, the first five books of Moses, and more specifically Genesis, in the English, it gives us to understand that before the last shift of the ages which caused a great flood, there was a man named Noah. He seemed to be the only one in his surroundings that really knew about the coming shift, and the scriptures say that he prepared himself, and made an ark to the saving of his household. After the flood there was a great rainbow and a message from God, that there would never again be such a destructive flood, and (...here is the punch line!), MAN SHALL HAVE DOMINION over the beasts of the field, the birds of the air and the fish of the sea. Well folks, I am going to tell you that for almost 5,000 years this entitlement has gone on and today the results are all around us. It does not matter if this false superiority exists between humans, or humans and other species. It is rampant. But guess what, those biblical words above are an *incorrect* translation from the Hebrew. Even Hebrew scholars have disagreed about it. The Rabbis that look at Kabalah and Earth Mother have no problem understanding the error. The original Hebrew beckons the human species to live in *"cooperation"* with all of God's species here on earth; not superior in any way. I have to ask you from your heart core if you believe that Creator ever projected such a false concept to Noah? Noah took a great a number of species into the ark... Is Mother Earth portraying that? [1]

Manifestations of what humans have accomplished with this false mandate of superiority puts a huge question in the human mind. **The question is whether they really feel they have value or worth without being superior?** We are addressing the bold-faced lie that humans are superior, that one race, such as the whites, are superior to the blacks (some say that they can prove it with the Bible!), and some blacks think they are superior to whites, and on and on, race after race struggles. The imperialistic destruction of indigenous nations - an ugly history - is still going on. However, the superiority that we are addressing here is really on a much broader scope- the entitlement to dominate, abuse, exploit, etc. every other species that lives and breathes on this planet, because we are humans.

The Kogi and Arhuaco indigenous Indians in Columbia believe we are so arrogant as to think that we can strip Earth Mother of Her gold and Oil minerals without thought or feeling. And in addition to that, they believe we are taking of Her very blood. To them, Gold and oil is the blood of the Earth Mother. They do not believe we are superior but equals to all species. Well, for 5,000 years or more, we have been duped. That scripture, misconstrued, outright incorrect, and whatever else you take the time to argue about, does not change the Truth that there is nothing in Nature, here on Earth Mother or beyond in the cosmos, that upholds that we are superior.

Take a moment to digest what this attitude has cost us. We are the only species that has messed this planet up. Not the birds, dolphins or any other species... JUST YOU AND ME.

Yet, with all this said, there is another point and perspective that should be mentioned. In our 'Level 2' retreats we invite native brothers and sisters to share with us their teachings, and stories about how to live close to Earth Mother. One sister that has come several times, a few years ago said, "Remember, dear ones, Mother Earth was doing quite well before humans were on Her. Respect Her or She has ways and permission to cleanse Herself of us"... WOW, did that speak to us! The quiet way that she spoke to us as an elder native sister whose heart is still close to Mother Earth, and who walks her talk. She is able to relate stories of how her ancestors did not espouse or believe the concept that humans were superior, in any way, to the rest of CREATOR'S SPECIES HERE ON THIS PLANET.

Folks, there are cultures that have never bought into a mere *translation* of a bible. Thank you Creator, for these blessed cultures that have never had such foolish thinking, and did not have this frame of reference to draw upon. And we are no less, or more, than all of our dear brothers and sisters that make up all of the species here, as well as everywhere else. But then, we have the individuals who yell and scream that some of their fellow humans worship the creation more than the Creator, yet they are the very ones who worship humans more than Creator. It is all a vicious circle of the blame game, which we do not see outside of the human species.

So how does Medicinal Aromatherapy work with us to counteract this disease that has so harmed us as a species? It literally brings us to our knees and puts us in a very delicious place, if we are willing. Mother Earth and medicinal aromatherapy will completely alter, forever, how you look at life. She will change your perspective and your belief system. Your own knowing will change.

I have been teaching both left and right-brained medicinal aromatherapy for a very long time. The left brain pertains to the dos and don'ts, the chemical analysis, the different chemotypes, organic chemistry, the blah, blah, blahs of the information coming from so-called scientific studies, double blind tests, gas chromatograms, electron spectrometers, etc. The right brain pertains to the emotional, spiritual, and even physical results of using pure essential essences for our well being. It is about understanding how Trees and Plants come from the Heart of Divine Love and how the deepest secrets come from that place of knowing, so, when we humans are ready, They beckon us to come to them, sit at their feet, listen, and remember all the beautiful things They will teach us. It WILL resonate with our heart core and we can remember wisdom and Her patterns. But, it will take surrender and vulnerability to do this.

Reflections

There was a student of mine about 7 years ago, Sally we will call her, who was an artist of Asian landscapes. She was also an author and was working on a book about, *"Angels in our Lives"*. I had been treating her for some time for physical and emotional issues via using the essences over and over again teaching her how to use them when I was not there. I desired to help her to remember to stay close to Earth Mother, when she related this story to me.

Many years before her and her husband were newly married and had been gifted with two boys. The boys grew and pretty soon they were 7 and 10 years of age.

Sally's husband spoke to her and said he desired to cut down a whole grove of Cedar Trees on their property so he and their boys would have a place to play ball. Sally said absolutely not, for the Cedar Trees are alive and conscious. She told her husband that they could play ball in another area of their place without hurting the Trees. They argued about this for some time and finally the husband gave in and left the Trees alone.

I had talked to her about speaking and listening to Trees and Plants during our aromassage sessions, so she decided to try listening by going out to her favorite place of meditation. Her favorite place of meditation was a chair placed right in the midst of the Cedar Trees that she saved 40 years ago!

Sally told me that one morning she went out to meditate at her favorite spot and she began to hear sounds which melted into words saying, "Thank You for saving us, Thank You, Thank You". She realized it was the very Cedar Trees that she had argued with her husband over 40 years previous. They were only baby saplings then.

She listened and then she told me how she became upset and almost insulted by the "thank yous". She then asked them why they waited so long to thank her and their answer returned, " Everyday for 40 years that you have come here to meditate we have been thanking you, but this is the FIRST TIME THAT YOU HAVE HEARD US because YOU WERE LISTENING FROM YOUR HEART. She said at 77 years old, this one experience changed her life.

---

[1] We are not talking about the food chain element of the survival of the fittest. That is another topic.

CHAPTER FIVE

Medicinal Aromatherapy Brings Us To The Remembrance Of What Surrender And Vulnerability Are All About

"Earth's crammed with Heaven, and every common Bush afire with God; But only He who sees, takes off His shoes- The rest sit round it and pluck Blackberries."

-Elizabeth Barrett Browning

"Little Flower, but if I could understand,
what you are, Root and all in all, I should know what
God and Man is."
 -Tennyson

"He who is born with a silver spoon in
His mouth is generally considered a fortunate person
but His good fortune is small compared to that of the
Happy Mortal who enters this World with a PAS-
SION for Flowers in His Soul."
 -Celia Thaxter

This is hard for us as humans today. We are in the midst of a great awakening, and the inevitable realization, that we are being controlled by other humans since the advent of the written word. We have easily given our power away to many people! Yet we cannot fathom surrendering and becoming vulnerable as humans. Surrendering to another species here on Earth Mother is just out of the question. We simply will not do it as we have numerous reasons conjured up in our minds. Why? Because we feel we are superior to all other species. Humans have been duped by one another, and surely, we will not let it happen on any other level. And, as if that were not enough, we do not trust our Mother. Here comes the 'Hamster wheel' time... Around and around we go, missing the truth about it all. If we would pause but for a moment, take a deep breath, and honestly accept in our hearts that all other species have more credibility than we do for echoing harmony and balance on Earth Mother, we then have no reason not to trust them, trusting them even more than our own species.

Huh, oh... better stop right here, put the book down, and meditate and ask your Creator, spirit guides and guardian angels about this.

Remember in Point Four when I talked about superiority? Even the Angels and Spirit Guides teach us about this. Superiority does not exist within the Divine Love paradigm.

So then, let us view the two possibilities of action, and the reality of what happens to us when we come to medicinal aromatherapy, and start working sincerely with the Tree and Plant Kingdom. One person who is left-brained and working with medicinal aromatherapy will view a Tree such as Spruce Red (*Picea rubens*), and say, "Hey there, Spruce Red, I've heard that you are quite good with your essence helping to bring about more awareness of what my passion in life is. I have also heard that you have natural cortisone properties that act as an analgesic for low back pain or sciatica. Hey, girl, give me your hand, and teach me what I should know about this, so that I can help my clients, myself, and others."

Now, the other person views the same Spruce Red Tree or Her pure essence as the first person but acts in the following way. "Hello, my name is Simcha and I have heard that you, Tasha, are a Spruce Red Tree, and can help me remember with your gifts. I've heard that you will permit me to sit at your feet whenever you call me, so that I may remember and learn from you when I surrender and have vulnerability. Which person do you truly believe will receive an invitation from Tasha, the Spruce Red Tree? The second one would be correct, because there is love, respect, surrender and vulnerability in her words.

Did you really think that Trees and Plants are so much different than us? Do you not agree, and know, that the Tree and Plant Kingdom are as intelligent and wise as we are? And guess what? Intelligence and wisdom are not subject to form, size, looks, etc. Those abilities come from Creator. Of course, true science and the how's of it all are also included. Let's remember once again that we will only draw to us what we are ourselves. We will mirror to ourselves always, nothing more, nothing less.

The gift of surrendering and becoming vulnerable is a very powerful gift to have in our very being. Look at the species all around us and observe. Observe the Tree and Plant Kingdom. At every turn you see these two gifts in action. It is beautiful to watch on so many levels. With the human relationships that we encounter, it is also beautiful to witness divine love when we surrender to each other, and become vulnerable for the harmony and peace of all that we desire. When two people are truly soul connected, walking in a relationship, surrendering and being vulnerable, this is the way of bliss! Each one acknowledges the other with acts of kindness, love and willingness... 24/7. It's not because each one has to, but because divine love constrains them and the heart desires to do so. Have you ever experienced what it was like to totally receive from your partner, no matter what level it was on? Remember, Earth Mother does teach us, from the beginning of our lives here on earth, that it is TRULY MORE BLESSED TO RECEIVE THAN TO GIVE. Hold your breath until you can't anymore and feel, experience what you do. You may have been taught the opposite, but what I have just said is what the Universe and Earth Mother teaches us everyday. Blessings to you as you ponder this.

Reflections

I want to relate this story about menopause and the essential essences. Barry and I had been recently married and moved all of my belongings in a 10' by 12' trailer and headed west. Upon arriving to my new home I began having a series of heart palpitations as well as night sweats. My passion and sexuality had decreased and I was crying allot which was not like me. I attributed all of this to leaving my home and family on the east coast and the newness of married life. The problem was that these symptoms didn't seem too be getting any better. Barry suggested that I might be in menopause and that I might consider using the essences.

Not wanting to admit that I might be in menopause, I absolutely refused. I was way too young to be going through the change. Well as time went on again Barry suggested that I needed to use the essences. Being the stubborn leo that I am of course I refused but went to some of my books to see if I indeed had the symptoms of a menopausal woman and Bam! I had all the symptoms.

So surrendering to the essences and my new husband, I started using the protocol that he suggested. I used Clary Sage, Geranium, Anise Raven to start with and almost immediately the heart palpitations stopped. I then added Melissa and Hyssop to the soup and I was on my way. Since it was summer time and it was really hot here in Arizona which didn't make the hot flashes any easier, I would drink Peppermint and Fennel in water several times a day which really cooled the chi. I am happy to report that within 6-8 months of using the essences daily, all of my symptoms disappeared and I was menopause free.

I now occasionally use the essences to balance my hormones when I feel the need.

Thank you Cynthia, my beloved.

CHAPTER SIX

How Medicinal Aromatherapy Relates And Uses Heart Feelings, Experiences And Explorations

"Different Flowers look good to different people. Pick the Flower when it is ready to be picked. The Flower that you spent time to care for does not grow while the Willow that you accidentally plant flourishes and gives shade."

-Chinese Proverb

"Every Child is born a Naturalist. His eyes are, by Nature, open to the Stars, the Beauty of the Flowers, and the Mystery of Life."
-R. Search

"NONE can have a healthy Love for Flowers unless He Loves the WILD ONES."
-Forbes Watson

First of all, let me say that there is a word in the English language that should be expunged from the dictionary and erased from our memory. That word is *experiment*. A word so popular, used constantly, on so many levels by us, yet so not connected to Divine Love or reality, even here on this planet. We may act it out as if we really believe it happens, but it is a lie. Experiment in the dictionary means a separation between observer and those observed. But when we are real and grounded, the reality of what is happening is that we humans are feeling, experiencing and exploring, not experimenting. What would you say to a date whom you were interested in, who popped the question to you, "What ya say, we experiment with kissing, and see how it goes?" I for one would be so turned off at such a belittling comment. I am not an experiment. My desire is to walk in Divine Love, which is all about feeling, experiencing and exploring life's journey with my wife, not experimenting with it as if it were a game or cold test.

Again, dear ones, humans have for so long separated themselves from the real truths that we are all connected, that Divine

Love is all there really is. Earth Mother is part of that Divine Love. Yet, for so long, we have experienced ourselves groping around in the dark wondering what happened to us? WE SHOULD REMEMBER THAT IT IS MOST IMPORTANT TO KNOW OUR LIFE'S PURPOSE. We have had masters, both female and male, down through recorded history, and, even more importantly, oral history, reminding us of who we really are. Most were killed because we could not stand what we were being told that the consequences would be dire if we turned a blind eye.

In the same way, left-brained medicinal aromatherapy drops the ball and constantly aligns itself with fear. In a similar way, the allopathic and pharmaceutical companies constantly indulge in experimenting -using tests galore. The ancients knew all about this without experimenting. No, instead they chose to explore it, experience it and feel it. Without their knowledge and wisdom, we would not even be here today.

How about waking up to the truth that what we call traditional medicine in this country is at best 165 years old and our ancestors survived for eons by Tree and Plant Medicine. The lies in school books and medical books about most every culture before us living such short lives due to poor health, etc. is nothing short of modern day terms of arrested development, heart and mental blindness. Past cultures everywhere used Tree and Plant medicine, lived wonderful lives and many lived longer than we do today. Alternative medicine is revealing this daily. Mindlessness has taken over so many of us because we do not desire to be bothered saying, "Just leave me alone and let me live my busy life pursuing what is called the American dream." It is time to feel and experience fullness of heart that mirrors the fullness of Divine Love.

The Tree and Plant medicine that our ancient ancestors experienced from their hearts, work for the harmony of all beings on Earth. This includes bacteria, fungi, viruses, parasites, etc., which, again, were here long before our human species came along. Our ancestors were very much aware of these truths. Not only are we more and more remembering the wisdom of our Egyptian, Babylonian and Sumerian cultures, but even those of the American Indian, Atlantean, Lemuria cultures. Are you aware that several years ago the International Health Association claimed that over 75% of the human population still used the Tree and Plant Kingdom solely for their medicine? Check it out, if you wish. I did not accept it at first either, but I can see how they came to that conclusion. But it certainly is not that way in the high-tech country where you and I live.

Medicinal Aromatherapy is successful when we feel the essence as one with us, communing with Her as a close friend, not a stranger.[1] Modern medicine does not teach us anything about feeling or experiencing Advil. Just take it. Quantum physics teaches us today that **ALL** things have energy and vibratory frequencies. Pure essences, pure herbs and synthetic drugs have distinct vibratory frequencies. The physical body has an affinity for pure essences and an aversion to drugs due to vibratory frequency differences. It amazes me the disconnect that we humans exhibit about this.

Many of us got excited, years ago when Deepak Chopra starting writing books on the rediscovery of quantum physics. We remembered that we are multidimensional beings having unique natural energies and vibratory frequencies. These frequencies are all directly linked to all the other frequencies that Creator has created. However, human-created materials also have a frequency, but not the same as Creator- inspired, harmonized frequencies. It is important to 'GET THIS'. Humans do not understand how to harmonize both the natural and the synthetic chemicals in drugs. The side effects are the conclusion of the matter. These are completely different from the original medicine that has always been and will be on this planet as long as She is alive and well.

Man-made medicine is something different. One thing for sure, pharmaceuticals are not healing the planet anytime soon, no matter how much they rave about their untrue cures[2]. We are talking here about the over-all picture. Just imagine what our society would be like today if the trillions of dollars that were spent on creating drugs, over the last 165 years, would have been used on reclaiming and remembering the truths and secrets of the healing powers of the Tree and Plant Kingdoms? We would rediscover the original medicine of Earth Mother.

So then, with the human consciousness from a heart of love, and with the heart mind, not the brain mind, we feel the essences. What does the pure essence of rose, steam distilled, do when I place it topically right on my heart? It enters my blood stream in 5 to 15 minutes, depending on my toxicity. What do I experience emotionally? What do I experience spiritually? Physically? Does it feel uplifting? Energizing? Clarifying? Encouraging? Peaceful? Calming? Warming? Am I willing to explore my broken heart with pure Rose or Guaiacwood to see if They will help me work through my story? This is how medicinal aromatherapy works, over and over again, when it is pure, The Trees and Plants love us and long for nothing more than to see us happy and living in harmony with Them and all other species here on our precious Earth Mother.

Reflections

There is a dear Arapaho brother who taught me how to keep the Fire in sweats. At the beginning of our relationship he was naturally dubious as to who this white man really was. He desired to be sure by following his heart that having a relationship with us was right. He desired to experience, explore and feel into us and asked for help from Earth Mother. We just kept talking openly and freely. Then one day I asked if he would be interested in coming over to our office and lab to feel it out for himself. He said he would, so about a week later he called and we set up the appointment. He arrived at our place, got out of the car and started walking toward the office. Audre, our business partner happened to be outside also at the time and her attention was drawn up to the skies. She saw this huge bird circling above our heads.

She gasped and yelled to us and asked our brother and me to look up.

As we were looking up, our brother yelped and said, "oh my god, that is sacred brother, the bald white headed eagle"... I now have my answer about our relationship... We will definitely work together". We happily brought him into the office and he immediately confided in me about how that he had been in the Vietnam War. He had contacted a dis-ease from the agent orange that was used so horribly in those days. I mentioned to him about several essences to use. I treated him that day with Fir Balsam, Eucalyptus gully gum (smithii), Helichrysum gymnocephalium and others. He immediately started feeling better and he could breathe better. Following his heart that day turned into a blessing for all of us. The bald eagle soared above for over 5 minutes around and around. Thank you eagle friend for your love also.

---

[1] The DNA of our make up spiritually, emotionally and physically fits like lock and key.

[2] The movie The Legend with Will Smith, once again reveals the disaster and absurdity of man's inability to understand. An intense movie, not pretty at all, yet created for many to see. Regardless of the motives for producing the movie, Creator and Earth Mother give us one more chance to view ourselves in the consequential mirror of life.

CHAPTER SEVEN

Medicinal Aromatherapy Reminds Us How To Listen To The Trees And Plants, And Follow Their Instructions And Guidance

"Don't try to force anything. Let Life be a deep let-go. See (God/Spirit/All that is) opening millions of Flowers every day without forcing the BUDS."

-Bhagwan Shree Rajneesh

"To analyze the charms of flowers is like dissecting music;
It is one of those things which are far better to enjoy than to attempt to
fully UNDERSTAND."
-Henry T. Tuckerman

The Tree and Plant Kingdom are unique species from Creator on Earth Mother. As mentioned before She gives us the four basic building blocks of life, carbon hydrogen, oxygen and nitrogen. Trees and Plants bestow upon us beauty, shade, shelter, energy, aid in drawing rain to a region, food, soil protection from erosion, filter pollutants, clothes, creates corn silk, hemp and medicine, etc. To explore how Trees and Plants do all these things, and more, is the beckoning that comes forth from Them to us. When we pursue divine love and peace, humility of true recognition of who we are and who we are not, the Trees and Plants bid us, "Welcome! Come sit at our feet, and we will teach you how to remember how we do what we do. We will show you how you can interact with us in harmony and peace without regret, shame or guilt."

All other species know what the Trees and Plants mission here on Mother earth is. When they see us come home to the Trees and Plants, they breathe a sigh of relief that humans have come home. Divine Love is the way home. As the original medicine of the planet, medicinal aromatherapy provides us with the means to facilitate healing on all levels of disease. No, we are not talking about applying essences on a compound fracture, expecting the essence to instantly set the bones, etc. Essences will speed up the healing with amazing results after the bones are set, just like they have done for eons. We are talking about dis-eases of the body, on every level, except basic skeletal breakages or severe massive injuries bringing almost immediate crossing over. Wars and cataclysmic disasters where we get blown up or smashed is not what we generally think about. Sad to say though, killing each other will never get us to where our hearts really desire to go. Listening to the Trees and Plants will put us back in touch with Source, True remembrance, True knowledge, True intelligence and True wisdom.

Now, let's get a bit more specific.

Exactly How Do We Listen Trees and Plants?

They do not speak the English language, or any language that humans speak, except one, the universal language from the inner core of our heart, accessed by believing in our intuition, believing in our feelings, believing our experiences. Did you get that? Read that last sentence again and again, if you think you should. Let's go further. Find a Plant and hold on to Her, or just hold a bottle of pure essence with the cap off up to your nose and start to breathe, inhale and exhale in slow rhythmic breaths. Get out of your brain mind and go down into your heart mind. Remember your heart has its own mind and battery system. We are not talking about your calculating mind in your physical head. In a calm state of surrender and vulnerability, listen with your heart ears for tones, or any sounds or thought patterns coming from the Plant or essence. In time your heart mind, your inner child, and your heart intuition will set in. By and by, the Plant Essence will begin speaking. How will you know? The tones will begin to turn into thought patterns in your heart mind. Your heart mind will then use your brain mind to interpret it into your own language, words and sentences, which will make sense. It will become a conversation indeed, and then as my mother told me long ago, "BELIEVE WHAT YOU HEAR AND NEVER DOUBT." I must tell you folks that, once this happens and becomes a part of you, it will change you and bring you back to source on so many levels. Your authenticity and integrity will be remembered, more and more, and will definitely affect your relationships starting with yourself first. Remember that the Kingdom of Heaven is within you.

I heard the story not too long ago about Geronimo, a famous Indian Chief from the Apache Nation. A few years ago, his great, great-grandchildren disclosed the real reason why the U.S. Calvary was never able to catch him or his clan. He always stayed at least 100-120 miles ahead of them. They say explicitly that he was a great shaman of the Tree and Plant Kingdom who was able to access Their wisdom on an every day basis. The desert Junipers and Creosote Deva's were able to show him through vibratory frequencies of the horse hoof sounds of the approaching of the Calvary, how far and where this enemy was. This gave Geronimo the knowledge of what to do next, to stay safe at a great distance from them. He was never captured but finally turned himself in. He has, of course, received a bad rap from history books, etc., but the truth is that he was a loving family man and in his enlightenment he was trying to save his people. So dear ones consider becoming students of the Tree and Plant Kingdom. They will never disappoint you, let you down or tell you lies. They will kiss you with Their wonderful energy and prepare you for the beautiful times that are ahead here on Earth Mother. Preparation will also include being able to understand and flow with Earth Mother through Her labor pains of rebirthing.

Reflections

This is a horse story that recently happened while we were on the Island of Rapa Nui. We had stopped for a lunch break with all 70 some of us. We were eating a beautiful lunch under Eucalyptus and Cedar Trees when Cynthia and I saw a gathering over around Drunvalo, the tour leader. We were just finishing up and chatting with the dear ones that we had chosen to sit down with under the Trees. We heard something about a horse being injured so we with our group gathered around to hear what was going on.

Mind you we had been treating people along the way of the trip with essences for various ailments and emotional break-downs. I heard Dru mentioning sadly that there was a horse with a new foal that had barb wire and smooth wire wrapped around Her left rear foot and some smooth wire around her right rear foot. The Mare had struggled so bad as to cut deeply into the left foot , maggots were on it, etc. I heard that we should pause and send Her good energy but there was really nothing we could do. I piped up and ask Dru, 'where is the horse and foal?'. Dru said back in the woods.

I felt this surge of urgency run through my veins and I quickly walked in the direction that I had been told. The head Shaman Benito and his son were there with the horse and foal, looking the situation over, talking between themselves and looking forlorn. My Spanish being poor and their English the same, we communicated with hands and a few words with body language. I looked the situation over, talked to the Mare and She ask me for help. She said She still had courage to live even though Her leg was deeply injured and infected. She told me, 'Barry my foal is not weaned yet and I must take care of Him'. My heart burst with courage.

I told Benito that the Mare desires to live. I quickly returned to the main group and told them what I thought. I could feel that there were a number of healers there that were not happy that all we were doing was sending good energy when it was time for physical action. Well, Barry went to work. I remember one brother from the Netherlands look me in the eye and ask, 'can we do this?'. I said yes, we slapped each others hand in a high five and got going. We rounded up barb wire cutters from our indigenous Brothers who were driving the buses, gathered up 6 men and walked towards the Mare. She ended up limping toward a large fenced area and stopped. A horse from the other side of the fence approached and literally kissed the injured Mare. I could hear the horse tell the Mare that everything was going to be all right. The Humans were here to help. As people know me, once I decide something, I am a force to be reckoned with.

The men were on both sides of Her holding Her still while I and two other men started cutting and unwinding the barb and smooth wire from off the badly injured foot. She stood completely still. Then, would you believe I actually that morning before we had started the days trip decided to bring two 15ml bottles of Clove Bud, one Helichrysum arenarium, one Cistus and one Thyme thuyanol, all full with me. I had others but this is what I intuited to put on Her foot. I poured one bottle after the other on it. It was just amazing to see how still She stayed while doing all of this.

We scraped the maggots off and of course the flies left quickly. One time I had looked to my right and about 20 feet away was one dear Sister Elder from the Maori Nation holding Her hands up toward us sending such energy that I could feel it strongly. We got the work done and let Her go. Just as this was being finished the baby stallion came right up to me, looked me in the eye and said, 'thank you so much for helping my Mommy. I love you and if it is okay, could everyone leave now? I am hungry and would like to suck '. Different parts of our group came back to this location two additional times to check on Her and She looked better each time and everybody was so happy.

This experience was a super bonding time for all of us on one level or another. I told one brother that this is what life on this planet is really all about. Knowing the do is not enough. We must roll up our sleeves and do the do. We chose a journey in this physical realm and we must from our hearts blossom in that.

CHAPTER EIGHT

Medicinal Aromatherapy's Abilities To Help Us Reconnect To Earth Mother

"A Tree once told me Her Story about how Earth Mother saved Her from Being cut down by loggers. She said now I can pass this on to you so that you know that as Earth Mother helped me, so I will help you."

-B. B. Kapp

"Though Humans come into the World live and whole,

the experience of

Those Beings that come into this World via an EGG is still ours also;

That is we must crack our shell if we are to live

Life to the FULLEST."

-B. B. Kapp

"In joy or sadness, Flowers are our constant Friend.

-*Kozuko Okakura*

I honestly wonder what the Tree and Plant Kingdom has for me to say in addition to what has already been shared with you. I have mentioned that this is truly a lifestyle. Reconnecting with Mother Earth is a joy of joys because there is every potential here to live happily ever after in peace and harmony as humans with each other and with every other species. Years ago, my business partner and good friend, Audre Wenzler, had a vision I would like to relate. She saw a huge table where every species was present (this included the rock people and insect nations), to discuss any and all topics of concern. Especially wonderful was the recognition, respect and honor for each one towards each other. From the dream she was hopeful that this reality would come true on this planet at some future time. The possibilities of bliss are endless.

Medicinal Aromatherapy, to say the least, is so very ancient.[1] It should be said that most books continually copy the next book on so many subjects of the fad of aromatherapy or true pure medicinal aromatherapy that it becomes disgusting and even nauseating to me. To give you an update, true medicinal aromatherapy is mentioned in cuneiform tablets, the oldest written language on earth that humans know of. The Sumerian civilization is much older than the Egyptian. In fact, in the written tradition it goes back at least 9,000 to 10,000 years ago. We have oral tradition like the Maori and Waitaha Nation from New Zealand, that talk about oral traditions concerning Manuka and Kanuka essences, going back at least 20,000 plus years.[2] So for those who need reassurance about numbers of years, there is plenty of references out there. So many that it boggles the left brained minds of individuals caught up in the medical illusions of today. Actually in another part of this book I have mentioned this, so that hopefully as many of you as possible who read this will understand.

The ancients, in both written and oral traditions, make it clear that they were taught about distilling the essences of Trees and Plants by the Star Beings at least 425,000 years ago! As you and I reconnect with Earth Mother via medicinal pure essences, truth, knowledge, intelligence, and wisdom will return to us, step-by-step. Earth Mother is on a fast track to help us reconnect with Her so that we get up to speed with what She is up to. It is one thing to be anxious, nervous and fearful about human behaviors and what the world of humans is doing; it is quite another to be up to date, speed and flow with what the Mother is doing. I am more concerned and excited about Mother Earth than about humans and their shenanigans. Our hope and trust should be in

Mother Earth. Remember again, Mother Earth points us to the Great Creator. She is going to help those of us who are desirous to be awakened in divine love consciousness to change the human dilemma. Do you believe that? Earth Mother is in direct harmony with Creator. Even my Hebrew background acknowledges that reality. The Crossing of the Red Sea was a definite acknowledgment of the cooperation between Creator and Earth Mother... and probably, the Star Nations as well.

I would like to end this point by saying that the Star Nations (Beings) are part of our family also. They have helped Mother Earth from the beginning of Her birth. We must wake up to the fact that Creator has multitudes of beings throughout the Universe who are full of Divine Love and have no consciousness of violence or killing that is rampant here. They consider us very un-evolved, yet realize Earth Mother desires to evolve much higher in consciousness and willing for any and all true divine help. Creator uses all of Her/His Creation to help in every way. Angels are just part of the Creation. It is plain in our own knowing that many times, we as humans call on Beings for help and guidance that are beyond our own capabilities. Angels and Beings from other star nations are highly evolved and set their attention and consciousness only to Divine Love, peace and joy, and harmony.

Reflections

Some years ago, one of my clients let us call her Mary, came to me for a consultation. She was an orthodox Jew and she told me very plainly that I would be permitted to touch only her feet, the top of her head, around the neck and no where else. She had overweight problems, respiratory ailments, and depression. We decided to work on the respiratory and depression problems first. We started the treatment with only two Eucalyptus essences, (*Dives* and *Radiata*). She said that they smelled horrible and that I should stop immediately .

We discussed the problem and though she truly desired for me to help her, she thought it would better if she left because she could not stand the smell. I convinced her to stay and said I would treat her feet only, if she were willing.

I told Mary that possibly it would take 6-8 treatments for her body to reprogram itself. Why?

When essences are pure and you do not like them, then those essences are the very first ones you should use. They are revealing an imbalance some where in the body, because the pure essences are completely harmonized by Mother Earth.

Weeks went by and faithfully every week, same day, same time Mary would come and I would treat her feet. After 6-1/2 weeks, during one treatment, all of a sudden, Mary spoke up and said, "You are using different essences today, Barry- aren't you? They smell good! " I told her, "No, they are the same ones- Eucalyptus dives and radiata- that I have been using from the beginning." She asked me to bring them up to her nose so that she could smell them. I brought them up to her nose and let her smell.

Mary looked at me and began to cry. She then told me that if she had not believed in me and the essences, she would have called me a liar, and left never to return.

However, she realized that for 5 weeks, she had been breathing better, and her respiratory problems were declining. She could smell like never before. She knew that the essences were the same all along. With her open heart, the essences facilitated a reunion between her body, spirit, soul and Mother Earth.

References

[1] The Trees and Plants tell me that they live everywhere in the Universe. Their covenant with Creator is the same everywhere. They have chosen to be the facilitators of healing and life spiritually, emotionally, and physically.

[2] Recently, I was honored to speak with an Elder from the Maori Nation concerning this. She said it is probably much longer than 20,000 years.

CHAPTER NINE

Medicinal Aromatherapy Facilitates And Helps Us To Believe In Ourselves And Gives Us The Will And Initiative To Take Back Our Power

"A Tree told me once that when Humans take their power back, they will stand tall individually. A Flower told me once that when Humans take their power back. They will BLOSSOM like a Magnolia. Many shall make a Flower Garden, or find a Forest and CREATOR will come and walk through it in the cool of the day. You will be like Us, the Tree and Flower told me. YOU ALWAYS HAVE BEEN."

-B. B. Kapp

"As Americans, we have become comfortable with our environment of concrete, steel, plastics, and artificial fibers, colors, and flavorings to such a degree that many question whether or not we even need to focus on a relationship with the CREATION. We have lost the desire to seek God and the ability to see God in all things. And perhaps, we have closed our eyes to the importance of GOD'S CREATION as expressed through the Forests because we have substituted the wonders of human creation for the wonders of GOD'S CREATION. This form of Idolatry should concern us."

-Susan Drake, The Global Forest 2000

One of the saddest realizations for all of us in these present times is that most of us do not believe in our own personal empowerment or ourselves. Even worst than that, we are awakening to the reality that we have given our power away to something or someone. The medical profession, the religious world, the political system, so-called terrorists, on and on, continue to rob us of our will and empowerment to be the 'grandest version of the highest expression of who we believe we are from moment to moment.' (Neale Donald Walsh's *Conversations with God*)

The Hopi prophecies make it clear that we are the ones that we have been waiting for- not something or someone out there in the ethers. True, with a heartfelt call we will receive help according to the divine plan, but we are still 100% responsible for our own actions. We are responsible to get our house in order and now is the time. 2012 thru January 2013 is approaching quickly, but the date is not important compared to you and I being close to Earth Mother, and prepared for the times ahead. Living in our hearts is the revealed truth. Labor pains are never pretty, but the birth will be marvelous and enchanting beyond what any of us can imagine.

My question to you is why have you given your power away to whatever? Are you asleep or awake to this? Do you even care? And if you desire to change, when are you going to do it? If you do not, why? You see, I am still asking questions, not to my mom or dad, but now to you. I would love it if you could be enthused with life enough that you would begin to seriously ponder these things. By the way, you came here by your own decision. No one forced you to come here. How many more lifetimes do you desire to go through the same lessons before you 'Get it'? This is your journey not anyone else's. You came by yourself through your mother's womb and when you leave you will leave by yourself. I remember years ago Deepak Chopra, a keynote speaker at a large conference, mentioning during his talk that he could not understand how and why humans all over the world create religions. Within each religion there is always a special place reserved for death and all that it means. He went on to say, "WHY? WHY? WHY?" As a medical doctor he had remembered that the cells in our bodies die or cross over constantly and new cells are being constantly born. Every 120 days our bodies go through a complete death and resurrection within the cellular structure. Every seven years the cells in our skeletal and bone system die and completely resurrect anew. So he said, 'We experience this constantly, which should remind us that this is our journey and no one else's.'

"Why do we create religions to remind us that we will pass at some point? This is usually a projection of many years hence; and many of us pay no mind to it at all, therefore, it holds no value as to daily reminding us that this is our journey alone here on Earth Mother. Instead, why not take our bodies as a living example of this truth and apply this to our hearts and heart minds". Deepak is so right with this truth. We must remember that again the Kingdom of Heaven is within us. Life and death is happening 24/7 within our very physical bodies. Our emotional and spiritual bodies also recognize this if we are awake.

The Tree and Plant Kingdom yield to land construction from humans, abuse from lumber companies, etc., but they stay on their path of harmony, peace and unity with Earth Mother and Creator. They can certainly show us the way to take back our power and sustain it no matter what other humans who desire to control, do to us. Divine love is more powerful than human control and those people who love control, actually do know this. In fact, these types of individuals don't desire for you to know that Creator created them too, and down deep in their core hearts, there still is a spark of Divine Love in them.

Reflections

On Thursday June 21, 2001 I heard the call to remember. Heeding the tug at my heart I contacted Barry Kapp and signed up for his Level I Medicinal Aromatherapy course scheduled to begin that Friday. The trail that ensued opened my heart to the truth and to deeply trust the higher wisdom that is beyond our dimensional construct. The following is my chronicle of a miracle.

As Barry eloquently discussed the purpose of the plant kingdom on the opening evening of his class, I thought that I had been drawn there for more than just learning about aromatherapy. The sense of urgency that had brought me this far was overwhelming. While I absorbed the class material, I prepared myself to let go and follow the unfolding to occur.

Early the next morning I visited my gynecologist for a follow up visit, prior to the start of the second part of level I later that day. Unceremoniously, my doctor announced that my PAP test came back abnormal showing that I had "high grade squamous intraepithelial lesion: severe dysplasia/carcinoma in situ: In other words I had level III cervical cancer.

Immediately I began to cry and as the tears flowed, I'll never forget the look on the doctor's face that seemed to say: "What are you crying for? This is repairable". Of course it is I thought, but that is the reason I was crying. What I had relearned in Barry's class was this. "Disease is the alarm signal of our consciousness, expressed through the body and therefore becoming... because we are deaf to the wispers of out heart and mind". He also taught that, "damage is created as a form of unresolved conflict blocked inside the body and that the plant kingdom exists to bring feeling into manifestation". These truths humbled me and I was ready to drop old patterns and any limitations that I was carrying within me.

I called Barry from my cell phone after leaving the doctor to inform him of my bad news. I asked him for suggestions on what essential essences to use to heal the cancer. Barry gently consoled me and gave me specific essences that I could use that had been used successfully in France to facilitate correcting this disease. He said with my permission that he would be sharing this information as a part of the course that day.

Upon learning which essences to use, I put them on a natural tampon for 30 days prior to my biopsy. I used Sandalwood, Frankincense, Galbanum, Myrrh, Parsley Seed and Cistus, which are known to have strong anti-cancer fighting properties. Lime, Mexican was added to the tampon for its anti-fungal qualities and to balance my pH. Cancer is known to develop when the body is in a highly acidic state. I also applied the Lime, Mexican on my abdomen area and on my feet. Rose was included to build the immune system and to help with heart issues such as lost, deep hurt and rejection. Rose essence made it possible to restore trust that made it possible for me to love again. I also used Cumin Black on the tampon and orally, 25 drops a day under the tongue to build my immune system. I also used Oregano linalool, which is antiviral and cistus for the immune system. I used Douglas Pine for the adrenals and Laurel leaf to cleanse the lymphatic system. Cistus was applied to the heart area daily. Last but not least, Cinnamon Bark a hot essence was applied to the bottom of my feet.

After 30 days of using the medicinal aromatherapy essential essences the results were remarkable. The pathology report stated that the cancer had reduced to a mild and moderate status. The oncologist stated that he wanted to perform a loop cone (LEEP) surgery, an extended biopsy under anesthesia, which was, scheduled exactly 30-days later. Approximately one week prior to my surgery, I was awakened from a dream where I heard that it was no longer necessary for me to go into surgery. I elected to go through surgery even though in my heart I knew that the cancer had disappeared. Four days post operation, the doctor told me the results of the pathology report. There was absolutely no cancer to be found.

Mother Earth is inviting us to experience a higher dimensional quality of healing and well being. It is an honor and a blessing to be beckoned by Earth Mother and to learn the disciplines of Medicinal Aromatherapy. My gratitude is immense and I will be forever grateful.

L.Brancey, Wisdom of the Earth Medicinal Aromatherapist: Thanks for your heart felt story. -B.B.Kapp

CHAPTER TEN

Medicinal Aromatherapy's Abilities In The Physical Realm Of Our Lives

"God has cared for these Trees, saved
Them from drought, disease, avalanches and a thou-
sand tempests and floods. But He cannot save them
from FOOLS."

-John Muir

"A few minutes ago every Tree was ex-cited, bowing to the roaring storm, waving, swirling, tossing Their branches in glorious enthusiasm like worship. But though to the outer ear These Trees are now silent, Their SONGS never cease. Every hidden cell is throbbing with music and life. Every fiber-trilling like harp strings, while incense is ever flowing from the Balsam Bells and Leaves. No wonder the hills and groves were GOD'S first temples, and the more They are cut down and hewn into cathedrals and churches, the farther off and dimmer seems the Lord Himself."

-John Muir

There is so much fun and joy to this point, because there is not a dis-ease on the planet that cannot be addressed, in one way or another, by pure medicinal aromatherapy. From cancer to heart disease to dermatitis to respiratory, all ailments have the potential to be corrected and maintained. Medicinal aromatherapy must be pure and not blended for this to happen. Additionally, every condition should be considered on its own merit and special. The question is, do we know how to access their secrets and ways in order to revive the correction and cure? Are we willing to quiet our human ego, which tells us that we know better, and instead just simply let Them work Their healing? If we can, then we will usher in a new, revived wave of contentment.

I am going to give you three analogies for why we do not dilute, blend, or teach blending. I mentioned about the wine analogy earlier. See what your friends would say if you served wine mixed with other wines, or dilute it in some way. Second... How about making a beautiful salad three days before your guests come to eat it. What do you think their advice to you would be? Third... A rainbow from heaven is so gorgeous with its unique colors, yet all are distinct yet separate. Blend all those colors together and you get the color brownish black!

Now lets have a chat about true quantum chemistry. Everything has a vibratory frequency and multi-dimensional capabilities. Every pure essence has a vibration special to itself. Shamanically and spiritually, the Trees and Plants, through the years, have made it crystal clear to me that They desire to be honored individually. When *chemotypes* get isolated, or essences get blended, it is like having 50 people in a room. I would single out one, take him/her aside, and we'd talk for two hours. Then I would bring this person back, and tell everyone that this persons' last name is Smith. I would summarize the whole Smith family after only talking to this particular Smith. This is exactly what Newtonian-based organic chemistry has been perpetuating for a long time. They create and study isolates and then summarize opinions about the whole essence, based on the isolate, instead of the whole.

And this same analogy also applies to blends. Yes, blends like Joy, Harmony, Auntie's Magic Tummy Harmonizer, St. Germaine's Ascension Tool, or Michael the Archangel's Insomnia Fix. They are a total lack of honoring to the Trees and Plants. Consider this: people say that you had better be careful with **Oregano** or **Thyme** because of the high concentrations of *phenol* in each individual essence. They claim that their studies, via the principles of compartmentalization, show them that phenols are potentially hepatoxic (liver toxic). Therefore, Oregano and Thyme are potentially dangerous. This is sheer craziness, un-evolved, even unscientific stupidity and it has done untold damage to our way of thinking in this modern world. Ever since Isaac Newton came on the scene and sold his wares- and the shadow forces that latched onto and ran with them- we have been thinking this way. Thanks to Quantum Physics, Quantum Chemistry and Sacred Geometry, we are reawakening and realizing that "Mitakuye Oyasin"-All things are connected to each other. Nothing is separate in the universe, ever.

Yes, *phenols* are definitely in Oregano and Thyme, but there are also many other chemotypes and constituents. Western European quantum physics and organic quantum chemistry studies have estimated that in any one drop of pure essential essence, (on a subatomic level) there are anywhere from 50-65,000 chemotypes, left brained, devas right brained all synergistically working together as one. So, when Newtonian chemists explore Oregano or Thyme from their perspective, they implant fear. They also lie because true science and spirit do not summarize or conclude a truth or a fact when based upon one part of something- especially if there is more than one part. Why? Because true science says the sum is more than its parts. Quantum physics or chemistry believe that multidimensional possibilities operate all at the same time, and therefore, to be true or even potentially accurate, one must look at all of the many chemotypes, together, and then try to come to some conclusion. To isolate one chemotype and summarize the whole plant's potential qualities, having no consideration for all the other chemotypes, is not correct. Every aromatherapy book that is using the principles in Newtonian Physics and applying them to aromatherapy studies is false. I know that this will make some people angry, but who will disclose this mess? You should, if you know this! It is just plain common sense, which I admit is hard to come by these days.

Mother Earth is the first one to reveal the falsehood of the Newtonian approach. Indigenous nations around the Earth know about it. Let's get updated from what I have gleaned in the last ten years- chemists have named a little over 1,000 of the potential total number of 50-65,000 chemotypes, including sub-atomic ones. To conclude this portion of this point, I love what my friend, Dr. Kurt Schnabelt, Ph.D. said in his book, *Medical Aromatherapy*, "The finer or deeper effects of oils still have to be evaluated individually, which throws the modern aromatherapy user back to old fashioned empiricism- gaining knowledge experience-by-experience."

Now let's chat a bit about different physical benefits of medicinal aromatherapy. They encompass almost any area you can imagine. I am going to give some examples and mention one or more essences that can facilitate help. I am not going to tell you the amount and all those particulars. Either you already know it, or contact us, or someone in the paradigm of love, who is a medicinal aromatherapist for the information.

Aphrodisiacs - *(there are many of them!)* - *Cinnamon Bark, Clove Bud, Nutmeg, Sage Clary, Vetiver*

Bed sheets - *Frankincense, Lavender family, Sandalwood*

Bone Pain - *Arnica, Birch Sweet, Frankincense, Savory Mountain, Spruce Black and Red*

Cancer - *Cinnamon Bark, Cinnamon Leaf, Citrus family, Cistus, Fir Balsam, Frankincense, Galbanum, Greenland Moss, Myrrh, Pennyroyal, Rose*

Central Nervous System - *Conifer family, Juniper Berry, Lavender family, Petitgrain family, Myrrh, Neroli, Rose*

Cerebral area – *Artemisia vulgaris linn, Helichrysum family, Rosemary family, Tamarack*

Cleaning around the house, floors, toilets, sinks - *Citrus family, Eucalyptus family, Fir family*

Digestive System - *Basil family, Coriander, Fennel, Ginger, Peppermint, Spearmint, Tarragon, Wintergreen*

Eyes - *Carrot Seed, Frankincense, Myrrh,*

Food - *Lime Mexican in salad, toubuli, egg salad, Orange in cookie dough, Tangerine, Rose*

Headaches - *Basil family, Peppermint, Niaouli*

Heart Disease - *Cardamon Seed family, Catnip, Goldenrod, Inula graveloens, Ylang Ylang*

Healthy drinks and teas - *Anise seed, Cardamon Seed, Coriander Seed, Cumin Black, Melissa, Peppermint, Spearmint*

Herpes 1 - *Cedarleaf, Mugwort, Myrrh*

Herpes 2 - *Frankincense, Hyssop officinalis, Melissa, Sandalwood, St. John's Wort*

Hormonal System - *Anise Raven, Anise Seed, Hyssop, Geranium, Melissa, Myrrh family, Myrtle family, Sage family*

Insect bites - *Catnip, Cypress: Blue, Emerald or Jade, Pennyroyal, Marjoram Sweet or Cineole*

Insect repellent - *Citronella, Eucalyptus Lemon, Niaouli, Palmarosa, Pennyroyal*

Insecticide - *Cinnamon Bark and Leaf, Natural concoction with Rosemary and Vanilla*

Insomnia - *Ajowan (hot), Chamomile Wild, Lavender Spike, Spikenard, Zanthoxylum*

Memory - *Helichrysum family, Peppermint family, Rosemary family, Sandalwood*

Muscle Pain - *Birch Sweet, Guaiacwood, Mugwort, Pine family, Spruce family, Wintergreen*

Perfume - *They all are the original perfumes of the human species*

Respiratory - *Eucalyptus family, Fir family, Myrtle family, Melaleuca family, Pine family*

Skin problems - *Chamomile family, Davana, Helichrysum family, Myrrh family, Tagetes*

Vertigo - *Calamus, Pennyroyal*

This is just a sampling of the many areas that can be addressed. I personally work with over 200 pure essences, which we ceremonially hand pour. I have the calluses to prove it! As I mentioned before, this is a lifestyle and life-long journey back to Earth Mother in all of Her glory. Our physical bodies are on loan from our Mother and every care should be taken to flow with Her in all areas of our lives. This can be joyous, but it is also work and responsibility. You do not have to be a scientist or doctor to use pure essences, however, if you are one of those humans that have never taken any responsibility for your own health, do yourself a favor and choose to change your ways. Take responsibility, take your power back, empower yourself. You will be the happy one.

You may surprise yourself immensely. Then, after your decision to walk in the direction of Divine Love, seek a love-inspired, medicinal aromatherapist who will encourage you in your empowerment and will not take your power away again.

Now, a note on 'hand pouring' in ceremony. We have talked about the reality of all things having a frequency of energy. One of the reasons pure essences enjoy humans is because of our similar frequencies. For example, when we hand pour with Native American music and our hearts are full of love, the essences feel that, and respond in a blessed way. The lack of human contact when the pouring is done with machines denies the essences that 'longed for' contact with humans even in the handling process. Believe me, machines do not carry the same vibratory frequency that humans do. Also humans who are not in Divine Love are different than humans who are. The frequency resonance is very different. If you are into real medicinal aromatherapy, you know exactly what I am talking about. As the song goes... "You know exactly what I am talking about!!!" Using divinely inspired music is also important, preferably non-verbal. Ask your essences about the atmosphere They like to be handled in. They will respond.

Concluding this section, I encourage you, dear ones, who have taken the time and energy to read this. Thank yourselves because it is not easy to change direction when profound lifestyle changes are being pondered.

My wife questioned me as to whether I should write so plainly, but if you ever sat in on my teaching, I would be no different. So why write any differently? Correctness without authenticity or integrity is just not my game. Again, all of us can truly be the grandest version of the highest expression of who we believe we are every moment of every day. If you think that is impossible, just take one moment at a time, then one day at a time. Apply a **Pine** or **Spruce** essence on you for grounding, **Rose** on you for self-love. Or you could use **Magnolia** or **Jasmine** for self-love. Folks, there are so many beautiful Devas out there that are still pure and unadulterated. So have courage, my dear ones. Let me balance all this out with a truth. With just about seven billion humans on this planet and untold numbers of domesticated animals, there is not even a fraction of enough pure essences being distilled by farmers to supply all of us.

But be not fearful. There will be enough in miraculous ways. How about the five loaves and two fishes story told by one master two-thousand-years ago? What about the stories of people whose gas tanks kept gas when they knew they were running out. They asked for help from their guides, which for some, even included the Trees and Plants, and they got where they were going without running out of gas. So the physical aspects of Medicinal Aromatherapy are truly endless with our *remembering* the width, breadth, depth and height.

Reflections

I was in France doing a farm tour with students. I was returning from a meeting with a seminar teacher when while walking down a flagstone stairway barefooted, I turned my right toe under, cutting it severely. Blood gushed out of the top of the toe and the pain was excruciating. I ran for the essences and two of my students noticed right away that I was in trouble. I first applied Cistus to stop the bleeding, then Pine, black for anti bacterial action, then Rose for soothing of the pain, fast healing, energy and last Helichrysum italicum for amplifying the the vibratory frequency of the other three. All of the students laid their hands on me for energy healing and the like. The next day was to be a long day of walking and touring with the farmers. I was able to accomplished the walking in sandals quite nicely with very little pain, stopping two times during the day to treat myself again. Some people thought that it was impossible to heal without stitches, but I did not agree because of previous experiences. After 40 days there was not a trace of scar on my toe that any wound of that severity had ever happened. Behold the power of the original medicine of Earth Mother.

In the fall of 2000 a client called me (we'll call her Mary) about Mackenzie her cat. Mackenzie was an energetic, playful, fun and joyful cat. One day after playing with Mary and some of her other cats, she appeared disoriented, had no balance, and fell over. Mary intuited that she had a stroke and took her to the vet. The vet confirmed that she indeed had a stroke and that it would take months to recover. He prescribed antibiotics though she really didn't want to use them. She might also have additional strokes or might not recover at all. Mary's intuition told her to call me to find out what essences she might use to help poor Mackenzie.

Within a few hours I drove to Mary's house to observe Mackenzie's behavior. Her head was cocked to the left and she could not walk as she was unbalanced and uncoordinated. It took about an hour of treatment. Mackenzie is a Persian cat so I had to pull the hair away from the brisket (heart area) to apply the essences. I also applied them on the back bone where the tail starts. I used rose, ylang ylang, juniper berry, frankincense and sandalwood.

Mary called the next day and within 24 hours Mackenzie could walk down the stairs, regained her balance and started eating. Within a few weeks she was well again. Mary could not be happier. One day several weeks later while consulting with Mary about a different issue, Mary asked if I thought that Mackenzie recognized the fact that I with the help of the essences, had helped her. Mackenzie was fast asleep on the floor about 15 feet from me and at the moment May asked that question, she jumped up, came right in front of my legs, rolled over and purred. Mary certainly had her answer.

CHAPTER ELEVEN

Medicinal Aromatherapy's Abilities For Our Emotional Dis-Ease

"Weeping may endure for the night, but joy cometh in the morning."

-Psalms 30:5

"What in your life as a child do you re-member most about the out of doors? Was it not a fra-grance, a smell from a Grass, a Shrub, a Flower Blossom, a Plant or Tree? Did it cause you to Move in your Emotional Body? If it did, please know that the Trees and Plant Essences in Their Purity can move and transform your whole emotional body. It has in-fluenced you and all of your Ancestors from the very beginning of our species. It is called JOY, PEACE AND HARMONY."

-B. B. Kapp

This is a wonderful topic to speak on; it brings tears to my eyes. Many of us are hurting from so many things and from so many stories. We have made ourselves victims of any number of things, people or happenings. Albeit, many of us are done with being victims! Finally, we have understood. Past stories no longer serve us. We remember that there is no judgment, no guilt, no re-gret, no shame, and no blame. It is not about sin anymore but about choices. In the dictionary, the word forgive is primarily speaking about a created human system that says there must be rewards for doing good, and punishments for doing bad, thus birthing the word forgiveness. Forgiveness should be replaced with something else, but that will take time.

Our Creator is all about Divine Love and not concerned about punishing us, therefore, not in the business of spending all this en-ergy that many humans emote as forgiveness. Creator never put forth effort to hold you or me on scales, weighing out either re-ward or punishment. Once again, humans have created this for control and power. This also is a telltale sign of the 'fear para-digm'. I am endeavoring to convey the root concept here. The act and desire to correct wrong or undesirable choices in our own lives is not what I am speaking about. Neither do I have a prob-lem with making things right with others that I have hurt in any way. Divine Love is about giving *us* the freedom to find our way.

If you create hell in your life, then get your fill and choose *love* to change it. If you prefer Divine Love, then walk in it and pass it on to your neighbor. It is not that we will not receive help but the choice is ours. Follow the path away from Divine Love and you go further into confusion, shadow, darkness, fear and nega-tivity. Duality does exist here, but in our heart core, there is no duality and we as a species are again awakening to this. There are absolutes in the Universe, not illusions.

At this time, do you desire to walk off the edge of a roof and psyche yourself up to believe you will not fall straight down and hurt yourself? I have always had problems with human authority. But Earth Mother's guidelines and the Universe's guidelines I honor from my heart.

The use of medicinal aromatherapy for our emotional well-being is unparalleled. If you would spend a day with us, listening to our phone conversations with those who call, you would soon know. Unfortunately, the drug world is not about healing, just bandaiding- with horrible side effects. There are very few drugs that address emotional problems in their many and sundry as-pects. In the end, humans will never be able to duplicate or mir-ror the original medicine of the planet. I am so thankful for this.

Oh, the pharmaceutical companies try, but they will always fall flat on their faces because they cannot recreate the identical vibratory frequency of the Trees and Plants. They either do not know or do not believe that, but they definitely do not desire that *you* know that! The news media has been giving many examples of what drugs can do to people. People on these drugs kill their families, themselves and others.

Here are some good examples of pure essences that will change your emotional life if you are willing to do the work. Remember, pure essences work under the canopy of non-interference between species, but They will help you to the door more quickly and easily so that you can do your work to move ahead. However, **They will not help if we do not ask.**

Abandonment issues and feeling untouchable - *Buddha Wood, Citrus family, Geranium, Hyssop, Lavender family, Violet*

All addictive eating disorders - *Citrus Family, Melaleuca family, Myrtle family, Spearmint*

Anger - *Hyssop officinalis, Jasmine family, Laurel Leaf, Lavender family, Thyme thuyanol*

Aphrodisiacs - *Frankincense, Highland Lavenders, Magnolia Blossom, Neroli, Rose, Ylang Ylang*

Aura Holes - *Chamomile, Blue, Clove Bud, Helichrysum family, Juniper berry family, Laurel Leaf, Rose, Tansy Blue, Tansy Wild*

Emotional blocks of all kinds - *Fir family, Helichrysum family, Mugwort, Petitgrain family*

Feeling far away from your spiritual family - *Balsam Peru , Benzoin, Buddha Wood, Roman Chamomile, Rhododendron*

Feeling far away from your spiritual guides- *Agarwood, Angelica Root, Balsam Popular, Frankincense, Tansy Wild*

Focus - *Citrus family, Peppermint family, Rosemary*

Joy and Happiness - *Chamomile, Wild, Clove Bud, Geranium, Lavender family, Neroli, Sandalwood, Spruce family*

Relationship problems, which start with yourself - *Fir family, Hyssop, Magnolia Blossom, Magnolia Leaf, Rose, Spruce family*

Self-esteem and love - *Ambrette Seed, Cardamon family, Fir family, Ginger family, Jasmine Sambac, Narcissus, Rose, Tuberose*

Self-regret, guilt, shame - *Agarwood, Guaiacwood, Hyssop officinalis, Juniper Berry, Laurel Leaf, Myrrh, St. John's Wort*

Transition and Ascension to the next level - *Catnip, Champaca, Lotus Blue, Peppermint, Pennyroyal, Spruce family, Wintergreen*

Working with a broken heart - *Agarwood, Guaiacwood, Rose, Violet, Ylang Ylang*

Working with fear, anxiety, angst - *Frankincense, Geranium, Hyssop, Laurel Leaf, Spruce Family*

Again, these are a few examples of what the Tree and Plant Kingdoms have to offer. Remember that the emotional and spiritual areas of our lives are the first manifestations of dis- ease in this dimension of life. When these are continuously not taken care of, they finally manifest in the physical realm. Also shamanically, every dis-ease is reflected on all three levels, spiritually, emotionally and physically. If you have a physical respiratory problem, there is an emotional and spiritual respiratory counterpart going on at the same time.

Reflections

This story is about a 64 year dear woman by the name of Barbara. She was from a very disturbed family where both the father and mother had sexually abused her continuously when she was a child. When she met my wife and I, years of therapy and work had been done. She had forgiven her father but her mother was an issue that just did not seem to desire to go away. Barbara told us that divine love had always been her only answer to the sadness and trauma that had followed her for so many years. Barbara was cheerful and sad at the same time constantly endeavoring to counterbalance the deep hatred and resentful she still had. She just did not know how to resolve the story and create a new story that would move her beyond her childhood. Also, she was feeling guilty that she had lingered with this for so long. She had done so much therapy, spent so money and still the same old hamster wheel. Why could she not let her mother go?   She was truly okay with her father after much work thru the years. We had a good consultation with Barbara and we enjoyed her heart-fulness and willingness to be so open. We laughed and cried allot together. We then proceeded to treat her on the massage table, both my wife and I working together with her. We bring the the father mother energy. We applied numerous essences on her as they called us for her situation. There was an immense releasing as the essences penetrated through her skin and into her blood stream. She yelled and screamed at her mother, telling her that all she ever desired was to be loved and not abused. She realized that her dear mother had also been abused and the hatred and acting out was just passed from one generation to another. Barbara was so happy that she called forth the power and strength to end this chain of agony. With Champaca, Hyssop and Frankincense on her crown and heart chakra, she entered into a deep dream state. We felt her mother there all around us, and heard her tell Barbara, "deep in my heart I loved you but I did not know how to show it with what had happened to me. I am so sorry my child. I love you dearly and I call forth these shackles to be loose from you, but you must do the work. The essences from the Trees and Plants are so loving, They will help you." After the session, she was truly different. She bought several essences and said the essences had facilitated a breakthrough for her like no therapy had ever done. Today we keep contact and she is on her ways with a new story and sense of well-being. Thank you essences for such great love and patience with us.

CHAPTER TWELVE

Medicinal Aromatherapy's Abilities For Our Spiritual Dis-Ease

*"It is always sunrise somewhere; The dew
is never all dried at once.*

*A shower is forever falling; Vapor is ever
rising. Eternal sunrise,*

Eternal sunset, Eternal dawn."

-John Muir

My thoughts go to the words of many masters from the past. One was Yeshua, the Jewish young man who said, 'Consider the lilies of the field, They neither toil nor spin, yet Solomon in all his glory, was not arrayed as one of these.' What was he really saying? First of all, this quote is from the King James Version in Old English.[1] Maybe we do not remember what toil or spin is referring to. It is all about creating, making, building and working. Solomon had so many workers to create the magnificent kingdom of temples, stables, homes, etc. Of course, history says he was a brilliant man. But, Yeshua is pointing out that, with all of this, the lilies of the field did not have to do any of that, yet they were far more beautiful than the beauty created by Solomon. When we, as humans, enter into the depth of this understanding, we will evolve so fast we will hardly realize what happened. To surrender and recognize the power of the spiritual realms and the contentment that follows, to know that we are all one in Divine Love is Peace, Centeredness and Creation itself.

Many circles of thought often talk and chat about the difference between being religious or spiritual. We desire to be spiritual, right? We are not interested in being religious anymore. That is like being political. Religion has an ugly track record, no matter how much denial, feeling insulted or evasiveness, you, friends, our relatives, or I might portray. Some maintain that you can be religious and spiritual. I say why doesn't water and oil mix together? Religion always separates on some level and certainly does not perpetuate harmony, peace and nonviolence towards all.

What truly is the big picture of spirituality? Is it not simply being in tune (right musical vibration) and flow (going in the right direction towards Source, Creator of All), which we are actually talking about? When we talk about spiritual things, often it is "way out there" somewhere, barely attainable. Yeshua said, "No, no." Access it and manifest it. This is what the lilies do. They have the Kingdom of Heaven within Them, just like we do. The difference is that They are accessing it to a much higher degree than we are. And They are **content** with it. The beauty is beyond comparison. Creator is in creation and creation in Creator. The same with us whether we tap into it or not. Everything on this planet that flows and vibrates within the frequency of Divine Love is spiritual. It encompasses so much- from the manifestation of Divine Love through caring, compassion, living in harmony and peace with each other and each species. Spirituality expands, evolving within Source, to open the doors that reunite all species and beings with Creator. This includes all of our relatives and family, even from everywhere beyond this Earth Mother. It is about knowing and having the wisdom, and manifesting power, to live like the angels and star nations all over the universe. Folks, it is just the big, big, big picture of the deeper breath, width and height of Creator's doings. This is what the lilies know and They manifest it.

That being said, Point 12 really has been portrayed exactly as it should be. You and I, with the help of other species have the potential to tap into Source and manifest peace, nonviolence, harmony. Do you remember the path back? They continue in it and are waiting for us. They are anticipating our return so that we can evolve together with Earth Mother to the next level of spiritual consciousness, reuniting with so many that have been anxiously awaiting this time.

So let us view a few spiritual dis-eases that the Tree and Plant Kingdom will address:

Chakra System Balancing – *There are 7 major energy points that we have heard of but my understanding is that there are a lot more than that: Frankincense, Lavender family, Lotus Blue, White pine, Spikenard, White Spruce, Sitka Spruce*

Living in the Heart and Not Your Mind - *Melissa, Hyssop, Rose, Sage, Purple and White, Sugandha, Tamarack*

Spiritual Aphrodisiacs - *Ambrette Seed, Champaca, Guaiacwood, Jasmine (grandiflorum officialis and sambac), Lotus Blue, Narcissus, Osmanthus, Sandalwood (santalum album and spicatum), Tuberose, Vanilla*

Spiritual Blocks - *Elemi, Rose, White Spruce, Blue Tansy, Violet, Yarrow, Ylang Ylang*

Spiritual Love - *Any and all-pure essences*

Spiritual Meditation Aid - *Champaca, Cypress Blue, Lotus Blue, Rose, Wild Tansy, Blue Tansy*

Spiritual Remembrance - *Lotus Blue, Narcissus, Osmanthus, Spikenard, Vanilla*

Spiritual Transition and Ascension - *Cypress, Emerald, Jade, Fir, Siberian Silver, Frankincense, Lotus Blue, Thuja Orientailis, Thyme family*

Unbelief in Source - *Champaca, Frankincense, Galbanum, Laurel leaf, Rose, Sandalwood*

So then, are you ready to flow with Earth Mother in Her Transition? Do you desire to stay or leave? Earth Mother is in Labor. Every species on Her is subject to Her Flow. Humans are just one of the species. We are the ones who should choose to remember because She will change whether we stay or not. All other species are more than aware of this and are acting accordingly. I hope this small book will help prepare many humans for what lies ahead. Just know that in the grand scheme of things, it is all about Love, Love, Love. Like one of my friends Chief Sonne Reyna, a Yaqui spiritual leader, says, "It really is all about Love, do not think about anything else, just Love." The Tree and Plant Kingdom bid you come and partake of that loving, awakening, remembrance, kindness and healing. They have helped our species from the beginning and are waiting right now to hear you ASK THEM FOR HELP. They will not help you unless you specifically **ASK THEM**.

From my heart to yours.

Reflections

This is a shocking story about a girl named Butterfly. She was in her 30's at the time of the phone call that came to me, asking if she could have a consultation and treatment. She flew here from another country and Cynthia and I greeted her and her finance John. We immediately realized that we had trouble on our hands. John said that as she boarded the plane, she literally could barely open her eyes and her mind was gone. She had taken steroid medicine before they had left and he was sure that it had affected her adversely. Butterfly's condition was cancerous lesions in different parts of her body including her head and skull, not the brain. Butterfly greeted us with her eyes closed and kept saying, "I am locked, loaded and ready". I had never heard that expression before. I proceeded to discuss the situation before us with Cynthia and John. We decided the best procedure would be to immediately put her on our massage table, and apply the essences that called to us to help her. About two hours later we finally were able to convince her to get on the table. During those two hours, it was literal hell. Poor Butterfly would scream, yell, curse at something inside her and then cling to John for help and security. Then Butterfly would apologize to Cynthia and me and that she was going to be okay. Once she was on the table, I started applying large amounts of Frankincense, Galbanum, Myrrh, Juniper berry, Hyssop, Rose, and many others. John was so brave but his stamina was wearing thin. We applied essences on him and he snapped right back ready for more. After three hours of talking, treating, holding and applying around 1500 drops of over 15 different essences, Butterfly all of a sudden started to make a turn around. Her breathing slowed down, her screaming, jerking, jabbering and flittering closed eye movement ceased. We were drained yet so happy for the results. We felt like a 1,000 entities had left her and she could finally realize peace and a sound mind. Butterfly started crying about how sorry she was and how embarrassed she felt about the whole experience. We lovingly talked to her for another hour or so while John held her in his arms on the couch. She said, "I was fighting for my life in my head all that time. It was like the drugs were a dark demon trying to kill her. All I could dwell on was trying to survive this battle raging inside of my head. I am so thankful for how you and

the essences helped me come back. I felt the essences wrap themselves around me in a ball of light. The dark demon of drugs
started backing off and I felt stronger to keep fighting. Then all
of a sudden the darkness, pain, and anxiety disappeared. I could
open my eyes and I was back." The spiritual help and power of the
essential essences from the paradigm of Divine Love had helped
Butterfly in a most extraordinary way.

---

[1] Matthew 6:28

PART 11

FREQUENTLY
ASKED
QUESTIONS

Every time you breathe in the Trunk of a Tree
Let the Roots crack parking lots at the World Bank Headquarters
Let loggers be Druids specially trained and rewarded
To sacrifice Trees at auspicious times
Let carpenters be master artisans
Let lumber be treasured like gold
Let soldiers on Maneuvers plant Trees and give police and criminals a
Shovel and a thousand seedlings
Let businessmen carry pocketfuls of acorns
Let newlyweds honeymoon in the woods
Walk don't drive
Stop reading newspapers
Stop writing poetry
Squat under a Tree and tell stories.
-John Wright

If what I say resonates with you, it is merely because we are both
branches on the same Tree.
-W.B. Yeats

Desire to be a Shaman?
Return to being a True Spiritual Human
Return to Earth Mother and Remember as much as you can
Sit at Her Feet and Be Quiet and Listen
Be Still and you will know Creator
Then Labels will vanish from your Conquest
But your deepest Desire for Peace and Joy will come Alive.
-B. B. Kapp

1. What About The Cost?

I say, "What cost?" We are living on this planet at this present time and I am not aware of anything that does not cost something in some way or another. I do not understand what people are really getting at. Maybe they should come clean and disclose what they really are trying to say? Are they saying that real pure essences should cost the same as adulterated impure ones? Do we have any other examples in the real world that we live in that could possibly answer this without spending much verbiage on it? Just remember that even cheap things are making money for someone or else they would quit offering it.

Folks, it is all about Life Force, not capitalism and getting the biggest bang for your buck. Life Force is within the vibration of Divine Love that includes fairness, equal for equal. If you desire to travel with us to see what it takes for farmers to create a pure essence, then come with us. You then can figure out what you make an hour or week in the form of money (LIFE FORCE). You can see if you are willing to be fair and loving with your pocket book. Every time I take people over to France to see a few of our farmers and their passion, sweat, time and work, they come back telling me that they will never ask about our price again.

I also desire to say something about the prices of essences and the difficulties that arise. First of all, the climate changes on Earth Mother are definitely affecting the Tree and Plant Kingdom. Secondly, humans have increased awareness of returning to Earth Mother for Tree and Plant medicine on all levels. This means an increased demand on facial products with essential essences in them, and neutraceuticals that have essential essences in them.

Most of these companies may have ultimately no concern for absolute purity, but they are creating more of an awareness of returning to the Tree and Plant Kingdom. Thirdly, we have animals that are not getting enough to eat because of lack of rain, and they are resorting to eating Plants that they do not generally eat. Two come to mind, **Highland Lavender** and **Helichrysum italicum**. All of this means scarcity, and that means higher prices for pure essences. Then there is all of the work, labor, time and energy that goes into the whole process.

Remember, life force for life force, and that includes the medium of exchange called money. You know, the money you work so hard for. So please do not create a double standard and get yourself to believe that what you make per hour or week holds more weight than what the farmers and we do. If you do not understand, spend your money and visit some of our farmers with us. You will never be the same on so many levels. Let us use the example of pure Rose otto steam-distilled. This is one of the most amazing essences to be sure that presently is available within Medicinal Aromatherapy. Due to lack of rain and increasing demand, the price just keeps climbing. If I desire to be able to offer it, I would desire to purchase it at the price the farmers feel that they should have for it. This goes for other essences as well. All in all, it is still amazingly much less than the over-all price of pharmaceutical drugs. Just remember that the prices for pure essences can change without notice at any time. All of the above reasons, and even more, apply for that to happen. I consider it an honor beyond words to be able to work with such loving individuals (farmers), and so should you. Without them there would be no essences at all.

2. What Do We Mean
When We Teach And Talk About Layering?

In my first book, *Wisdom of the Earth Book and Reference Guide*, there is an article that I wrote years ago entitled, *Tips on How to Use Essences Wisely*. In that book I discuss the marvels of *layering* instead of *diluting* essences with carrier oil. Let me quickly tell you that you can use many cool (Yin) essences on the skin 'neat'; i.e. the hot (Yang) essences you sandwich between two cool ones un-diluted, and the hot ones will assimilate nicely with the two others and not cause an irritating reaction. Example, **Vetiver** first, then **Cinnamon Bark** second, **Juniper Berry** third, making sure that the hot **Cinnamon Bark** essence stays within the perimeters of the yin cool essences.

There has been so much written about diluting essences with carrier oils that I am not willing to believe that there is that much ignorance and lack of common sense out there. I believe there are other reasons for so much effort put forth about the need to dilute. Perhaps it has to do with lessening the effectiveness of the essences. In other modern words of today, "dumbing" down the essences so that They will not perform at Their ultimate potential? In another part of this book, I have written about this quite vividly. I also have written about blending, which is just another facet of diluting. All of this changes the vibratory frequency of the pure essence. By the way, some have tried to challenge me with the comment, 'Well, you blend by layering.' There is a big difference between using pure essential essences at the time of need, layering one on top of the other, and inviting the molecular intelligence of the pure essences to commune with the molecular intelligence of the physical, emotional, and spiritual body of a human; and that of taking six (or even more) pure essences and pouring Them into an empty amber bottle, creating a blend, putting a name to it (Angel Michael's Insomnia Tonic), and using it over time, which could be who knows how long. Mixing essences, even pure ones cancels out the vibratory frequency of all the essences.

Pure, undiluted essences, as long as They are stored correctly have a shelf life of several thousand years, believe it or not! That is according to findings from archeological discoveries from the Valley of the Pharaohs in Egypt way back in the 1950's. Blends do not. In fact, I have had the unhappy experience of testing many blends with a crystal pendulum, only to find that usually, within 12 to14 hours the vibratory frequency of that blend is gone. I have shed tears about this already because humans are so unbelieving and stubborn. They think that they can improve upon something so beautiful in its pure state without adulterating it. They end up with a fragrance and placebo effect, but no vibratory frequency because it has lost its power. Layering is so simple and just plain works. No further explanation has to be brought forward. Dilution is an illusion based on the Fear Paradigm. And if you are using impure essences it does not matter what you do, as they are already compromised and there will be consequences in some way.

3. Some People Ask... and Some Say That Aromatherapy Is Raping the Earth

This is an amazing reverse psychological ploy used again by the dark side. Maybe there is some merit to it where the fad of organic ways, the fad of aromatherapy, the fad of herbology, etc. exists which is again motivated by the Fear Paradigm. Remember the duality clause that the human species still lives under at this moment? But those of us who desire to live in the Love Paradigm do not rape Earth Mother, we flow with Her and partake in that which She has to offer in a non-invasive manner. Using sustainability protocol, Lavender is always growing back, as well as, all other plants used in medicinal aromatherapy. Spruce trees are harvested by clipping only the outer most branches and needles allowing, the branches to grow back. Farmers keep track of these trees and give them respite so that They can stay healthy and grow back. If the Tree passes over, the Farmer will ask permission to use large parts of the tree by chipping it, soaking the chips and then distilling them. These are just some examples. When it comes to the companies that work outside the Paradigm of Divine Love, then raping is in order quite often. Also male energy disrespecting the female energy and placing such on Mother Earth is still very much alive. Hopefully this will diminish very soon. Harmony and Balance should be our desire.

4. A Few Additional Thoughts On Blends

I spoke about it above. I should share one additional item with you. The Trees and Plants have often spoken to me like this: "Why can't you, as humans, respect us like you desire to be respected between human and human. We know you do not respect each other, much, but those of you who desire to, know we are no different. We would like to be honored for who we are and what we offer as gifts to you. Allow a Lime essence to be Lime essence and do not blend us into something of your own choosing. Would you like us to do that to you? If you desire to use more than one of us at a time, fine. Then layer each one of us, as we call to you, one on top of the other, when you desire to use us. Then permit us to do what We will between Us and the one desiring our help.

5. The Words Oils and Essences?
What Difference Does It Make?

Again, I have spoken about this before in this book, but suffice to say that these two different labelings- oils and essences- have caused a dearth in comprehending what this is really all about. I know some humans are very glad for that, but I for one am not amused. Pure Essence is the lifeblood or quintessence of the Plant or Tree, just like human blood, or the blood of a animal. When the essences are pure, there is no greasiness or even residue left within minutes. When pure essences are absorbed into your blood stream within 5 to 15 minutes, you are receiving Their very Life Force. The magnitude and results are Life Changing. As we awaken to the Ancient Ways of Wisdom, it is one of the gifts They bestow on us from the beginning before we were here on Earth Mother. Their covenant with Creator is enduring as to Their desires for purpose here. Their desire was and still is, to facilitate healing spiritually, emotionally and physically. Nut oils are wonderful and we use Them a lot. They have Their own personalities and also have special qualities but are not the same. The two should not be confused. There is enough confusion in aromatherapy already. Nut Oils are greasy, takes a long time to absorb into the skin. Nut oils and essences are not the same. Lets allow a nut oil to be nut oil and a pure essence to be a pure essence.

6. What Is Hand Pouring and How Important Is It?

Hand pouring is the opportunity to spend time with the essences and engage with Them in conversation. It is a golden opportunity to listen and it is especially to listen to Them tell Their stories of re-membrance, knowledge and wisdom to us. By the way, they also have plenty of wit. The vibratory frequencies of pure, single essences maintains a continuity with human handling that does not happen with machines made out of metal and operated with electricity (AC current). Valerie Ann Worwood speaks in her book, *The Fragrant Heaven's*, that it is also very important **who** is pouring. She mentions that there is also importance as to **who** is using the essences. This is absolutely so. The point is that fear driven aromatherapists or hu-mans who use aromatherapy, block their own blessings and facilita-tion of potential healing. Why? **Because Pure Single Essences work from a Paradigm of Divine Love only.** So, the essences keep-on loving, but the person's fear can block or dilute the desired results. That simple. That deep. That's not so simple. So both hand pouring and working from a Paradigm of Divine Love are imperative for success with the Trees and Plants, and also, tapping into Their deeper wisdom, keeping in mind who is teaching who.

7. So You Think Integrative Medicine Really Works?

Another sore topic that is so easy to understand yet so difficult for those who think that Fear and Love can ultimately exist to-gether. The answer is no. It may appear to work here and there, but in the end, it will not. Two different paradigms, two different vibratory frequencies. Do War and Peace ultimately live together in the same bed? I don't think so. Thanks, but no thanks, for trying to mix the two. A case in point; what we have found and experienced to be true is that anytime pure essences are used or mixed with drugs of any kind, *if* there is any canceling out, it is the drugs that are nullified, not the pure essences. This includes Homeopathy too. Again, dear ones, we are not speaking of adulterated essences. Pure Medicinal Aromatherapy will integrate with any other medicinal approach that is operating from the Paradigm of Love and the same vibratory frequency.

8. What About Animals and Medicinal Aromatherapy?

If you allow your domesticated dog or cat out of the house when they are not feeling well, you watch them. What do you see them doing? Eating dirt, chewing on grass, biting on the bark of a Tree. Being a retired dairy farmer and cash crop farmer, I have had the opportunity to watch many animals use their instincts and knowledge to make use of the Tree and Plant Kingdom. Animals will teach us so much if you take the time to be with them. I must say here though, that the domestication of dogs, cats, and cows, over the eons, has caused quite a bit of harm to their inborn intuition and overall well-being. They are contracting the same dis- eases (supposedly) as we humans. How interesting and disturbing. And I am one human who does not believe everything someone tells me about how their dog or cat has this aliment or that ailment just like us. Someone told me recently that their dog has Lyme disease. They say their vet told them that. I say Bull#*# or maybe I should say Dog#*#. My father was also a dog trainer. He brought me up with St. Bernard's. Chows, German Shepherds and Pugs. They were allowed outside all of the years I was growing up. I never saw one of our dogs get Lyme dis-ease from a Deer Tick or wherever they think it comes from. I know times have changed, but I believe we are projecting our dis-eases on them. And some of them are taking on our emotional traumas because they love us so much. How about letting your dog or cat be a bit more a dog or cat and quit trying to make them human. You might learn a lot from them.

Animals definitely respond to pure single medicinal essences in a big way. One should always consider dosage based on weight and by asking enough questions about the dis-ease of the animal in question to be able to intuit the right essences for them. Also asking proper questions helps you to hear the essences call you when They are ready as to which ones to use. This goes for humans also, of course, that is asking them the right questions.

I have read over and over on the Internet about how cats cannot absorb essences through their liver, therefore it should be taboo. If that is true, then why have I used pure essences, according to their weight, over the last thirty years and had many cats respond by getting well and going on with their precious lives? I heard that there have been tests done, etc. That has not been my experience. Again, are we approaching this out of a paradigm of love or fear? Also, I believe there are just too many people out there using impure essences. All discussion is off if this be the case.

9. How Do You Know If The Essences Are Pure Or Not?

Here is a great question I have been asked 100's of times over the last 10 years. I wrote several articles on this and I will summarize this subject for you. Medicinal Aromatherapy is a journey, a lifestyle for sure. Right now in the U.S. there are supposedly only around 8 to 12 companies that have truly pure, hand poured essences, but I am not here to write about that. I am saying this... technically a pure essence absolutely has no additives or subtractives in it. After the water or steam distillation you get what you get. When it comes to absolutes or concretes, and after the necessary filtration, the ppms (parts per million) are beyond detection. Absolutes and concretes use natural solvents during distillation, and after the filtration, you get what you get. Any playing with the essence at all from the harvest to you the end user- is considered not pure.

Did you know that the fad aromatherapy companies can put on their bottles 100% pure essential oil as long as it starts out that way. What they decide to do after that, they are free to do without letting you know. This is our good FDA at work. However, you *can* know, if you are walking the journey of medicinal aromatherapy, if you are able to smell and taste and feel the energy from it. Here is where taking 100% responsibility for your actions and decisions come in to play. Do not expect someone else to do your work for you. Physicians hardly know what is in the drugs they prescribe or hand out as gifts to get you started. Their drug sales reps do not know most of the time either. So please do not expect allopathic people, hospitals, etc. to know anything about medicinal aromatherapy and the Tree and Plant Kingdom. In medicinal aromatherapy we talk about personal relationships with the farmers, the essences and with our clients. This is about reuniting with the family that is returning to Earth Mother for our medicine on all levels. So... how can you know? By using them, smelling them, tasting them, getting to know those that hand pour in Divine Love and seeing if they are real or not.

Are these people authentic? Can you actually contact them or do they give you the run around? Do the people have integrity or is everything a trade secret? In the real world of medicinal aromatherapy we actually invite you to visit some of our farmers with us on tour. See if you can do that with most fad aromatherapy companies. It is not that I am saying trade secrets have no merit at all, but ultimately the time for secrets is over in every area of life on Earth Mother. I have been asked how I deal in my own heart with so many bogus aromatherapy dealers out there. I am glad for anyone that in some way helps to bring people back to our roots, but that does not mean I am going to follow them and neither should you. Trust the Tree and Plant Kingdom that They will direct you and show you the way. Ask them. Remember?

And lastly, let's chat a bit about the modern way of testing essences for purity. I am talking about the gas chromatogram test and the electron spectrometer test. Again, humans can make a machine do most anything they want whether integrity is there or not. It means very little to me because my desire is to visit and create a relationship with all my farmers as much as possible so they know my heart for purity and I know theirs. We desire to be on the same page. I am most interested in building relationships with these farmers because they are farming bio-dynamically or wild crafted. They are usually small farmers interested in quality and not all about quantity. It has been disturbing to me to hear different ones through the years express to me (left brained well meaning aromatherapists or suppliers) that if an essence does not meet the specs of their machine tests, they would not use it. OH

MY! Do you know that most of the information that has been put in the machines was gathered some 20 to 30 years ago? Do you suppose that the Trees and Plants are evolving over that period of time to survive the conditions on the earth just like humans are? If so, much or all of that information is obsolete unless they have updated it. Also, these machines are very limited in their information that they spit out because we as humans have so little information to put in. The sub atomic parts, (chemo types), of essences are not put in these machines for information because, again, we do not know. So my answer to some who have told me that their product is pure, natural, nothing added or subtracted or better yet wild crafted, and it didn't meet the "machine" requirements, was, "call me and I will take those essences off their hands, and hand pour it in ceremony." Then I will be blessed in using it myself and offering it to others. Again the two paradigms come clashing together and will not mix. Sad but true.

10. How Do I Test And Decide On The Pure Essences I Offer To Others?

By my nose. Which, by the way, is still the final authority in places like Provence, France. A nose is the final authority if the machines malfunction. It is the, (Trust Name or Authentic Backup), in the business. Even in perfumery, noses' have high priority. For me, I smell and smell and then I taste. I build a trust relationship with my farmers who supply our essences. And lastly, I use an ancient method called, "Crystal Pendulum Energy Vibration Testing". It consists of me taking hours with different samples I receive from several of my farmers around the world. The pendulum will swing to the left or right or back and forth if the sample has any life to it at all. This method with the Tree and Plant essences has taught me much through the years.

11. What About The Importance Of Our Farmers?

Let's talk about the farmers who so graciously plant, grow, harvest and distill the essences. They prepare the essences to ship to me so that I can continue the bonding with them through hand pouring and the like. Blessed be the farmers. I wish we had more humans in the U.S. who would feel called to serve their fellow humans in this way. Being a retired farmer myself, both dairy and cash cropping, I can verily identify with them. It is hard work, the rewards are great but getting rich is not the first priority or goal. Yes, some do very well after years of hard work and grace and patience, and so they should. Even on our end, it has not been uncommon to spend 10 to 12 plus hours a day keeping things rolling. Farmers are just as passionate as we are here at Wisdom of the Earth. They are our family whether they are in Egypt, France or Canada. We work with about 50 to 70 farmers around the world. We do not know each other's languages, most of the time, but we know each other's heart. We do have translators who are also part of the family. Many tears of joy have fallen from my eyes, my students' eyes, and our farmers' eyes as we sit down to eat together in their homes, feeling their love and hospitality. Our language is spoken from the heart and it feels so good, so peaceful, and so harmonious. You would be surprised how we can communicate without speaking hardly a word of each other's native tongue. We speak through the Trees and Plants to each other and it works.

I remember being in Nepal a few years ago, where about ten of our essences come from, visiting one farmer who is a soul brother to me. My soul brother's father, a shaman, is around 86 years old, met me and we sat together on the floor and ate meals with our hands most of the time. About half way through our visit, (two weeks), he came up close to me, looked me in the eyes, smiled at me with his warm deep eyes, and proceeded to stroke the back of my head to half way down my back. He just kept on doing it and speaking a prayer in Nepalese. I just cried and then his tears begin to flow and then my soul brother began to shed tears. My soul brother, who could speak quite good English, told me what his father was saying to me in the prayer... "Forever special to me, forever bonded with me". These are the kind of farmers we work with. Remember, we can only mirror to us what we are ourselves.

12. Let's Talk About The Question Of Side Effects With Pure Medicinal Aromatherapy Essences

I know this is hardly talked about in Medicinal Aromatherapy, except from a Fear Paradigm. We have those skeptics and naysayers from the Allopathic realms who conspire in one-way or another. However they are intimidated by the truth that their short-lived security in that which does not truly heal is being eroded away by alternative medicines of any kind. So then what about side effects from the Tree and Plant Kingdom? There can be little. I say, a little compared to dying, due to the side effects of drugs prescribed or otherwise. The numbers of people crossing over due to the side effects of drugs is indeed staggering, but not surprising. The principles within this book would make this fact easy to figure out. What, then, are the side effects of using pure medicinal aromatherapy, in my experience? One would be breaking out with a rash or small itchy bumps on the skin where you apply the pure essence. Why does this happen? In my experience it is usually due to the amount of toxicity in a person. Physical toxicity is one thing, emotional and spiritual toxicity is another. The greatest form of toxicity that humans must deal with on a day-to-day basis is emotional and spiritual.

The essences, working from a paradigm of Divine Love go into the cellular membrane, into the outer blood capillaries, into the arteries to commune with the body and they together begin to work. If the individual has a lot of stuff that does not flow with love, the body can begin to discharge the toxins so quickly that it creates a rash of some kind. Secondly, it can be from skin sensitivity. A good rule of thumb is to ask for their Sun Sign in Astrology. Each sign has a different skin type sensitivity. This information is ancient and is very reliable. Go to your skin specialist if you will, your psychologist or modern doctor, but I will tell you that Astrology is an understanding of the bio-rhythms of Earth Mother and how She relates to things and beings on Her, In Her and above Her. Find out where the left brained professors get their information and I will tell you where the ancients got their information.

So, a very important part of Medicinal Aromatherapy is to ask questions when you are called to help someone; in this case, skin rashes due to application of pure essences. Thirdly, it can be a combination of both high levels of toxicity and skin sensitivity.

How can this be managed? Through finding out about the person before applying the essence. Start out slowly with few drops of pure essences (a normal sized adult around 8 to 10 drops). Finding out what the condition is, is of vital importance to know. If a rash of any kind starts, stop applying it on the location and go to the bottom of the feet. The bottom of the feet can take any essence and it will be absorbed into the blood stream as well. When in doubt, go to the bottom of the feet. Speak to the essence(s) and ask them for guidance. When They tell you, listen to Them and remember for the next time. After the rash is gone, go back to the same location and apply half the amount that you did in the beginning. Watch and see how that goes, and so forth and so on.

This book again is not meant for telling you a bunch of protocols, formulas, etc. Take a class where true medicinal aromatherapy is taught for that. This is a journey back to the original medicine of Earth Mother. It must be more energetically transferred than just reading a bunch of words on paper. You can do that with putting together a cabinet from IKEA but not the Tree and Plant Kingdom.

13. Are There Any Other Side Effects That Are Important To Mention?

In my experience working with Herbs and Essences for over 40 years, the rash is the main one that pops up from time to time. And, by the way, people do overcome the rash. When I started years ago with the essences, I started using Laurel Leaf over my heart for courage, strength and stamina, as well as lymphatic cleansing. It took me eight months to overcome a rash that I got. I kept going back and forth between my feet and my heart. It worked, and today Laurel Leaf does not in any way give me a problem rash-wise. I am sure it would if I became toxic again in the areas that it helps me in. I did my work also.

Side effects of burning eyes can happen, but that is usually due to the high oxygenation of the essence aroma fumes getting into the eyes for a bit at the beginning of the application anywhere close to the eyes. That is not a problem. Over dosing is a possibility but usually the essences are not that inviting to do such a thing. I find the love and power of the essences so interesting and amazing. I do not know of one recorded case of intentional suicide with pure essences. I believe that there is a great protection in this realm with the Tree and Plant Kingdom, unlike the drug world.

I do know of the famous case years ago where a woman desired to abort her fetus. The story goes she took about 60ml of an essence. The story goes on to say that taking the essence was the cause of her crossing over, but her baby lived. If this is true, then it was a very unwise choice. And then there is a more recent story reported a few years back on a British Aromatherapy Database Company, a young boy (around 8 or 9 years old) took 60 ml of Cinnamon Bark over a period of hours. He must have really loved it because She is hot. He became inebriated, felt sleepy and was rather out of it. He threw up and within 8 to 10 hours was back to normal. Can you imagine taking 60ml of Ritalin or Prozac and what the end result would be? Common sense is so important!

Some people come to me and tell me that the essences give them a strong headache. I ask them why they come to our lab and office, then, if they believe that they are allergic or are going to get a headache from the essences. Many times I have seen that these very dear souls are blocked because of an emotional experience from the past that has never been resolved. I ask simply about that and I have witnessed many amazing break-throughs. **Also be assured that impure essences can and will give you a headache.** It is not good for you just like other synthetic or adulterated smells we smell around the world today.

14. Any Other Side Effects? An Additional Thought

None that I can think of through my years of experience and using the essences myself. Remember, we are talking about the side effects of the essences in comparison to the extreme side effects of every drug made. Just by taking a pill, what are the possible consequences? That is the same as what I am addressing here. Medicinal Aromatherapy is not about a little amount of essences is good and more is even better, over the long run. It is about correction and then maintenance. The pure essences are facilitators; you still must do the work. They are amazing, but They never take away your part. They always desire to remind you and give you the space that you are amazing and powerful. **They do not desire to ever take your power from you. Drugs do.**

15. Is Medicinal Aromatherapy Truly A Lifestyle?

The answer is **YES** or should I ask you what part of Yes don't you understand. After reading this book I trust that you will see like you have never seen before. I would like to add some quotes right here from others that have spoken to all of us at one time or another. Again, all of the quotes are pointing in the same direction.

I'd rather have roses on my table then diamonds on my neck.
-Emma Goldman

Where flowers bloom so does hope.
-Lady Bird Johnson, *Public Road: Where Flowers Bloom*

Each Flower is a Soul opening out to Nature.
-Gerald De Nerval

Perfumes are the feelings of Flowers.
-Heinrich Heine

Flowers are Love's Truest Language.
-Park Benjamin

There came a time when the risk to remain tight in the Bud was more painful than the risk to Blossom.
-Anais Nin

If there were nothing else to trouble us the fate of the Flowers would make us sad.
-John Lancaster Spalding. *Aphorisma and Reflections*

There are philosophies as varied as the Flowers of the field, and some of them weeds and a few of them poisonous weeds. But none of them create the psychological condition, in which I first saw, or desire to see the Flower.

-G.K. Chesterton

Who can estimate the elevating and refining influences and moral value of Flowers with all Their graceful forms, bewitching shades and combinations of colors and exquisitely varied perfumes! These silent influences are unconsciously felt even by those who do not appreciate Them consciously and thus with a better and still better fruits, nuts, grains, vegetables and Flowers, will they be transformed. Man's thought refined, and turned from the base destructive forces into nobler production. One which will lift him to high planes of action toward the happy day when the Creator of all this beautiful work is more acknowledged and loved. And when man shall offer his brother man not bullets and bayonets, but richer grains, better fruit and fairer Flowers from the bounty of the Earth.

-Father George Schoeneer (1864-1941). *The Importance and Fundamental Principles of Plant Breeding.*

16. What About the Shaman's Way in Medicinal Aromatherapy?

Often people have asked me if I am a shaman for the Tree and Plant Kingdom. Labels are a dime a dozen but what is manifested in a person's life tells it all. The dictionary says that a shaman is one from tribal origin who inquires from the invisible about many things, including healing and uses magic, sorcery in the process and then brings it back into the visible. I believe there is a lot of misconception about this definition. Then on top of that, the human ego gets in there, and yes there are many who call themselves shamans. My dear ones, it is still true that a Tree or Plant shall be known by Their fruits. So it is with humans. Feel your feelings and your experiences about anything you do or see or partake of or indulge in. Trees and Plants have taught me that they only live in the paradigm of love where duality does not exist. Therefore, any experiences with them are from the love paradigm. I believe the original shamans are those who not only go into the invisible, but also sit at the feet of other species that Creator has created. Why? So that we may remember to love and work together in harmony from these other species and realms. They help us to remember to work from a paradigm of love only.

This attitude that we find in the dictionary and other places smacks a bit too much of a religious point of view. If that be the case, then anything that opposes someone's precious belief system is suspect, and the connotation is askew. The Tree and Plant Kingdom have always been in the Light and if you choose the dark, I do not believe They truly respond. It is an illusion. If something happens, it comes from a source other than that which is in harmony with Creator. The idea of duality here on Earth Mother is very vivid indeed and also used to evade responsibility for 100% for our actions. But blessings abound when we live in our inner heart core. We are remembering that there is no duality there.

17. EXTRA...
Surprised That Pure Essences Actually Work?

Several years ago at a conference a medicinal aromatherapist stood up and mentioned that he finds it so amazing and strange that when we, who use pure essences constantly, see true facilitation and healing take place, we are so *amazed*! Why is this?

As I have inferred repeatedly, for a long, long time, we have been programmed not to trust Earth Mother, and that includes Trees and Plants. Once we know and feel the security that we receive by trusting the Tree and Plant Kingdom via Our Mother, we find that this experience is more encompassing than trusting humans first. When I was fifteen years old, my Dad told me that by the time I was eighteen I would either make his way my way or I would not. What was that way? He taught me to trust Earth Mother and the Trees and Plants first for any and all of my medicine and humans second, if at all. I chose my father's way at eighteen.

Recently my wife and I were with the Mayan Elders in Guatemala doing ceremony in preparation for the Earth's shift around Dec. 2012 – Feb. 2013. There was a young man with our group who had an intense awakening in one of our ceremonials. Earth Mother showed him the reason why he has so much trouble living in his heart and prefers his mind. "You don't trust me She said, you are afraid of me". His conversation with Her revealed that there had been many natural catastrophes in his life and family and it caused huge fear. He came to resolve those stories and made a commitment to himself and Earth Mother that trusting Her was much safer than trusting humans. Why? Because it works. And so it should. Medicinal Aromatherapy works too. And so it should.

18. What Is The Difference Between Essences and Herbs?

First, I would like to let you know again that my Father was a self-taught herbalist. He taught me all he knew about the wonders and healing powers of the Trees and Plants. So I honor herbalogy immensely in its original simple form. There are many Trees and Plants today that are not distilled yet into essences. In herbal form is the only avenue to obtain them. You can also procure them yourself from the forest, meadows, mountains, etc.

Pure essences are many times more concentrated than pure herbs. Some studies suggest well over 1,000 times more. As I have already written in my book about the oral tradition history of these two, I will leave it to you to explore, experience and feel the differences and similarities. When pure, They can both work in concert together. However, the herb dried or ground up has a miniscule amount of essence in it, if any. The essence is like the hospital of the Plant or Tree. When Plant or Tree material is distilled, the steam breaks down the essence sacs and is the catalyst for the sacs to release the essence. The essence is extremely concentrated. The pure essence is the most potent medicinal facilitator on Mother Earth. We are slowly evolving. How wonderful. I trust this answers the main questions that come my way about true medicinal aromatherapy.

PART III

MEDICINAL
ANGELS

Barry Kapp with wife, Cynthia.

1. AJOWAN

LATIN NAME: **TRACHYSPERMUM AMMI**

FAMILY NAME: APIACEAE

Ajowan is relatively unknown in the United States, but is famous in India. Her strong pungent smell can actually push one away, until one decides to go for a more intimate meeting. I have had some clients say that at first it smells like burnt rubber tires. It is one of the Angels that quickly reveals Herself and She stands right up front with no masks. Her anti viral properties are renowned in India and Asia. Ajowan is a strong persuader and any enemy molecule that is in your body will cringe at realizing that She is entering the body in which it resides. Ajowan is also known well for Her ability to relieve deep-seated insomnia. Placing around 8 to 10 drops on the bottom of each foot, (for a normal 130-165 lb. adult), doing reflexology, you can expect results. She has generally +/- 45% thymol, not unlike the Thyme or Oregano families. This means that She is a HOT essence to the skin, and for beginners especially, the bottoms of the feet are suitable. *(All essences can be neutralized by a good grade of nut oil...washing your hands with a nut oil after using a hot essence, or if you happen to rub your eye, because it is burning and you forgot that you had an essence still on your fingers.)* Ajowan is also one of the essences that will give you a telltale sign as to how balanced you are. If you are not balanced, nausea can occur. She will strongly help you correct that. Ajowan is also helpful with gas, dispelling those pockets very quickly when topically applied to the stomach. By layering a cool essence on either side of Ajowan and allowing Her to assimilate with the other two essences such as Basil and Wintergreen, you will not have a problem.

Ajowan also addresses deep-seated congestion. I am always blessed in remembering how many of the Deva's aid in all levels of respiratory problems. This is on the spiritual, emotional and physical planes. She will definitely address deep seated blockages caused by our many spiritual or emotional stories that we are still holding on to. Did you know that the scientific data coming out of research in Western and Eastern Europe suggests that the essences that you cannot stand are the ones you need more than the ones you love? The research states that the unpleasant reaction is revealing a disharmony in your being. If you commit to using the unpleasant essence for 6-8 weeks, generally your physical being will reprogram itself to balance. And you can count on actually enjoying the fragrance. You should also prepare yourself for the reprogramming of the emotional and spiritual areas that Ajowan will address. Ajowan has been known to accomplish this for many individuals. Essences are always balanced if they are pure and unadulterated, and they will slowly and carefully help to balance you. Ajowan is Yang in Her energetic nature, which means that though She is feminine, Her energetic qualities are masculine. Though She is strong, firm and full of clarity, Her love will show forth as the fruits of Her labors unfold.

> *Find expression for Sorrow, and it will become Dear to you.*
> *Find expression for a Joy and you will intensify its Ecstasy.*
> -Oscar Wilde

11. CARDAMON SEED, GREEN

LATIN NAME: ELETTARIA CARDAMOMUN

FAMILY NAME: ZINGIBERACEAE

Dating back well before the 4th century B.C. in Greece, Cardamon Seed (Green) had graced Herself before Humans with a Yang presence and more specifically a feminine-masculine personality. Growing from South America to India, and to Sri Lanka, She prefers elevations from about 2500 ft. to 5000 ft. above sea level. She is a perennial growing to 15-feet-high. Her flowers are pure white with mauve markings, opening up in the form of a yoni, pure Shakti. On one of the larger petals there is a red design in the form of a Tree with branches, the trunk starting from the base of the petal. One could say that this design resembles an artery with small capillaries branching off everywhere. One could also see the symbol of "The Tree of Life" in Her. She is a major gift bestowal for the heart.

Elettaria cardamomum is one of the oldest mentioned spice plants in the world. Each pod contains upwards of 20 aromatic, dark red-brown seeds. Research in the 60's affirmed the ancients use of the volatile oil for its strong antispasmodic properties. Elettaria cardamomum is an inhibitor for digestive conditions such as: gas, farting, colic and cramps. She is famous in India as a facilitator for clearing bad breath, urinary incontinence, a great heart tonic on every level, and good for asthma, kidney stones, anorexia, sexual debility, bronchitis, weak *vata*. She is an amazing 'chi warmer' for those struggling with cold or weak Chi. She has an ancient reputation as a hormonal aphrodisiac.[1] She is wonderful for morning sickness, energizing and uplifting along the way.

Elettaria cardamomum taps into the corridor that leads us to our higher selves in a gentle and positive way. She warms our heart to believe that we can go forward successfully when we find ourselves overburdened with the journey of life. She, in Her warmth, expels fear, being stuck, frozenness, gives us feelings of courage, stamina, patience and strength. She whispers to our hearts, "Oh my sweet one, you can be true to yourself. You do not have to betray yourself anymore. You can be strong with gentleness, softness, tenderness and love." For those of you who have not yet started a relationship with this Deva, you are missing a powerful and strong ally that will stand beside you as a personal friend. You will feel Her hugging you so deeply that your life force essence will burn brightly.

The most evident token and apparent sign of True Wisdom
is a constant and unconstrained Rejoicing.

-Michael Montaigne

---

[1] Remember, all pure essences work on the physical, emotional and spiritual levels in unison. So, as an aphrodisiac, She will work to harmonize all three levels. Be prepared to do your work.

Visual Manifestation of the author's dream

2000 + year-old Olive Trees in France

Barry Kapp with Arhuaco and Kogi in Guatemala

Lotus, Blue on Island of Moorea

Essential Essence stills in France

Wisdom of the Earth product line

Barry Kapp with ceremonial flute

Jasmine in Corsica

Old portable still in Provence

III. CHAMOMILE, WILD

LATIN NAME: ORMENIS MIXTA

FAMILY NAME: ASTERACEAE

Though there are many species in the Chamomile Family, some stand out in the world of Medicinal Aromatherapy more than others. Yet, when one considers all the species that are out there, the farmers have distilled very few of them in large quantities. I recently met a farmer in Morocco who has played with several species of the Chamomile Family, distilling them, smelling the essence, etc., but going no further. The species he played with are unheard of in the Aromatherapy world, but it first takes passion such as his to introduce new essences. If some were not willing to take a risk, we would not have the essences we have today. Why? Because when you're a farmer, money is a factor, just like for anyone else, unless you're a "gentleman farmer" for whom money is not an issue.

Chamomile, Wild (*Ormenis mixta*) is one such essence that is still relatively new to much of the world, but not to Morocco. This beautiful Deva grows wild about two hours drive from the city of Casablanca. The plants grow upwards of four to five-feet tall with strong, red-tinted stalks. The bright white flowers, with a magical soft golden ring of yellow coming up from the base inside of the flower, create a sea with waves, flowing back and forth, of these Devas. It is as though they are in a great concert with a specific message of love, tranquility, calmness, wisdom, and care. The beautiful *Ormenis mixta* is part of a much larger family known as the *Asteraceae* group. Among botanists there is a feeling that this family is of the most highly evolved Plant species. This plant family reveals that beings on this planet can co-habit for the well being of the whole, expressing individuality, yet in a non-separating, non-exclusive way. Experiences with this Deva range from an aphrodisiac, liver disorders, anti-anxiety, skin disorders and respiratory problems to blood purifying. My business partner, Audre, had a profound experience with Chamomile, Wild about six years ago. Audre used Her to wean herself off anti-anxiety/anti-depressant drugs like Buspar and Serax in a matter of six weeks (against her doctor's orders!) Another experience concerned a woman whose job was to deal with irate customers. She started using Chamomile, Wild and the essence facilitated focus, clarity, self confidence and an ability to think rationally with no fear. Chamomile, Wild had facilitated handling her job better. I have many clients who use it consistently for all types of insomnia. This Deva folds Her arms around you and lets you watch the concert with happiness and direction. Such a huge range of possibilities! How can this be? In the Medicinal Aromatherapy world, trust, relationship and experience are always present. Sadly, many humans have regarded as valid someone else's experience instead of their own. They're in relationships that are not truly intimate, and they have little trust in themselves. However, they may have some trust in other human; just enough to project responsibility off of themselves and on to someone else. Through exploring, experience and feelings, our ancestors obtained an understanding of medicinal uses spiritually, emotionally and physiologically from the ancient past all the way up to the present. Then, about 125-165 years ago, the pharmaceutical and the Allopathic philosophy came into vogue. They chose the Paradigm of Fear and claimed Hippocrates as their Father. If you read what Hippocrates believed, you will discover the falsehood in their claim.

Humans are now awakening. Remember, the Plant and Tree Kingdoms have had millions of years to remember about harmony within themselves and between themselves. Chamomile, Wild is one such special Deva. By watching Her, the ancients used Her and saw that the way She acted in the fields directly related to how She would work with humans and animals. In the day we are living, this Deva exudes strength with confidence, calmness with wisdom, and blesses those who come to Her with wide-open hearts by showing what really matters. Our nervous system longs to commune with such a Deva as Chamomile,Wild. The shadows are great today, but the Light is even brighter. Chamomile, Wild is in the front line for Her White Bright Light. May She bless many.

"If I can bring Joy into the World, then I'll be successful."
-Bobby McFarrin

IV. CISTUS

LATIN NAME: CISTUS LADANIFERUS

FAMILY NAME: CISTACEAE

Cistus has Angelic qualities that are very extra-terrestrial, and very little has been written on Her compared to other essential essences. Why? Because we are just beginning to remember what Mother Earth has given to us for our overall well-being. This evergreen bush creates large, beautiful, white, red and pink flowers. Her smell is unlike anything you are familiar with, and yet, She has been on this planet for eons. Ancients around the Mediterranean knew of Her and raved about Her immune stimulant properties. All one has to do is breathe Her in for one minute to feel the distinct, sharp, but all encompassing complexity of Her personality come forth. HER SENSE OF WELL-BEING JUMPS INTO YOUR AURIC FIELD AND YOUR BODY SAYS... "Ahhh."

Cistus is also called **ROCK ROSE**, which implies a queenly quality like Rose but an earthly firmness that grounds you into a solid being of whatever species you represent. As an extreme immune stimulant, She nurtures and facilitates harmony on all systems of the body, emotions, and spirit. She is known as one of the most instant wound healing essences we have at our fingertips. She works instantly with bleeding conditions along with **Helichrysum** *italicum* or *arenarium*, three of the most instantly effective blood coagulators to clot blood fast. She works the best externally but will also work internally. I have used both the steam-distilled and the absolute essence of Cistus on skin cancer with amazing results, both alone and layered with other essences. Cistus works very well on skin tags, both pre and actual squamous or basal types.

Cistus is Yin in temperature and Yang energetically. Her chemotypes, (left brained) or Devas, (right brained) are numerous just like all other essential essences but write-ups usually include *pinene camphene* and limonene, which are all well known for their anti-bacterial, antiseptic, anti-tumoric, anti-cancer, and respiratory abilities.

Cistus works wonders for the central nervous system, helping to regenerate harmony.

The flowers of Cistus are beautiful white, pink, or reddish pink. The petal texture has a ripple-like appearance. She tells us that anti-aging for the skin are one of Her fortes. Emotionally and spiritually, She will strengthen your immune system and keep it young, vibrant and earnest. Her leaves and branches can be sticky to the touch, so She aids you in commitment, steadfastness and the ability to stick to something and see it through. She also enjoys well-drained soil and will pass over quickly with too much water. She loves balance and is very sensitive to the needs of Her body. This is a good lesson for us. If we trust Earth

Mother completely, She will show us constantly what it takes to stay in harmony with Her, which will totally balance our individual desires. Take time to create a relationship with Her and you will know what I am talking about. She will become one of your best friends.

The Flowers take the Tears of Weeping Night
And give Them to the Sun for the Day's Delight.
-Joseph S. Cotter, Sr.

V. CLOVE BUD

LATIN NAME: SYZYGIUM AROMATICUM

FAMILY NAME: MYRTACEAE

Clove Bud is an evergreen Tree, growing up to 50 feet in height with a strong aromatic air all about Her. Very ancient memoirs talk about Her being quite well established on the Molucca Islands of Indonesia. **Clove** was such a highly traded substance that it is said that ships coming into the harbor could smell Her pungent aroma even before landing.

Memory and the whole cerebral area are very stimulated by applying 10 drops on the crown chakra every day for 5 days on, 2 days off, for a total of 14 consecutive days. Then rest for two weeks, and repeat the sequence. Digestive problems such as bloating, colic colitis, gas, nausea, etc. can greatly benefit from the **Bud of Clove**. Viruses, fungi, and parasites do not like to cohabitat with Clove Bud. Apply a few drops on the abdomen before sharing your love with another human, and experience what an aphrodisiac She can be. We use Her to treat acne, skin sores, skin ulcers, and sties. The quantum multidimensional uses of Her are many, and it is so easy, as with all of the other essences, to forget to think of Her when a dis-ease arises. The Deva eugenol, in its purity, isolated from pure Clove Bud, was the original numbing agent for dentists for many years until they believed a synthetic reproduction was better and they could make more money. For me, Clove Bud just simply spells C-LOVE in a most divine and celestial way. She is a great energy booster when the "blahs" set in. Today, with the different maladies that are appearing, due to Earth Mother shifting, or such pollutions as chemtrails, Clove Bud is a powerful ally to have in your portfolio. Though many claim out of fear that you cannot apply Her directly on the skin that is far from the truth for those who choose love. Always do a test patch first and please make sure your essences are pure and not adulterated in some way. Applying Clove Bud neat on the skin works most wonderfully, warming the skin but not burning it. You can choose to layer Her between Myrrh, Manuka or Kanuka. That works wonderfully, too. Clove Bud is a great friend of mine. She says, "Use me for all areas of neuralgia, such as sciatica, for I have a good anesthetic effect which is even more effective when I'm used with St. John's Wort and Peppermint. I come to you at such a time as this to calm you and help you pass through the eye of the needle, which is fast approaching." Blessings to you as you walk circumspectly.

"Then I was standing on the highest mountain of them all, and round about beneath me was the whole Hoop of the World, and while I stood there I saw more than I can tell and I understood more than I saw.

For I was seeing in a sacred manner the shapes of all things in the Spirit, and the shape of all shapes as they must live together like One Being.

And I saw that the Sacred Hoop of my people was one of many Hoops that made One Circle, wide as Daylight and as Starlight, and in the center grew One mighty Flowering Tree to shelter all the Children of One Mother and One father. And I saw that it was HOLY."

-Black Elk Speaks, *The Great Vision*, (1932) p.36.

VI. CUMIN, BLACK

LATIN NAME: NIGELLA SATIVA
FAMILY NAME: RANUNCULACEAE

Nigella sativa has provided much encouragement and aid to people suffering from immune and autoimmune dis-eases. We have many people taking this to keep themselves in balance, having some of them comment that they just do not desire to be without it. So they keep several 4-ounce bottles on hand and if they live in more than one place, they keep one at each of those locations. She is called the, "Magical Egyptian Herb for Allergies, Asthma, and Immune Disorders". The Prophet Mohammed raved about *Nigella sativa* and said, "**Black Cumin** heals every disease except death." Today in the Mideast, our farmer says that with the 'Awakening', regarding climate change and the coming shift of the ages, the farmers are having a difficult time raising enough just to supply the Islamic nations. We are blessed to have the relationship we have so that we can offer **Cumin, Black** to our friends and family in this part of the world. She has special abilities to aid in clearing all dermatological problems of the skin.

She works with viruses to help clear them out of your body. The overall fatigue that is raging all over the Planet can effectively be addressed by Nigella sativa. The chemtrail travesty that is affecting so many of us is also being tackled by Cumin, Black. Now, let's talk about allergies and asthma. She will absolutely help facilitate less sneezing, less itching of the eyes, less congestion in the head by using one half teaspoon at least twice a day orally. You can also prepare a marvelous tea with some pure honey and a half-tablespoon of Cumin, Black. She is so soothing to your whole being. She works with prostate problems on every level. She also aids in clearing and correcting Hepatitis ABCD, HIV and Herpes 1 and 2. Cancer has been addressed for many years with Cumin, Black with continued success in helping humans and animals correct the problem. Of course, this also means living an overall lifestyle in every area of life that supports healing. I leave you with a quote that I hope will bless you.

Did you measure to attain your height?
Did you use geometry to radiate your limb?
Did you lament storm-torn branches?
Did you inventory your leaves for the Sun?
You did none of these things. Yet Man in his cleverness
Cannot match your Perfection.
-Deng Ming-Dao

VII. Cypress, blue northern australian

LATIN NAME: CALLISTRIS INTRATROPICA

FAMILY NAME: CUPRESSACEAE

Discussing this gorgeous Deva is fascinating and mysterious. *Callistris intratropica* is a new distilled essence for modern mankind, but She is ancient as all other conifers are on this planet. Ancient cultures, such as the Tiwi's of the Bathurst and Melville Islands, (in the Australia area), knew of this Tree. The Tiwi's have inhabited these islands for at least 15,000 to 20,000 years and have made use of Her extensively for their health, well being and ceremony.

Today, botanists gave Her a Latin name, *Callitris intratropica* from the *Cupressaceae* family. Then in another area, there are the political struggles, power and greed that mankind places on one another, over and over again. This also includes the illusions that these types of people place on their own, so-called underlings;

THAT MOTHER NATURE IS NOT TO BE TRUSTED. Contradiction after contradiction, yet they cannot bypass the truth as to who has been USING AND TRUSTING THE TREES AND PLANTS, before their personalities entered the picture.

Farmers, who have chosen to harvest *Callitris intratropica*, have met up with such circumstances; therefore some register Her only as a "Cosmetic Excipient." Actually, that is of little consequence, since the distilled essential essence is speaking loud and clear to all who experience Her. Her Deep Caribbean Blue color brings to mind the eternal blue of the sky and heavens during the day here on Earth, helping to harmonize our heavenly and earthly origins. It is thick like Sandalwood, (*Santalum album* or *spicatum*), Vetiver, (*Vetiveria zizanioides*), or Guaiacwood, (*Bulnesia sarmienti*). Using my crystal pendulums of carnelian, rose quartz and amethyst, I find Her to be Yin, Feminine in energetic nature. She is definitely Yin temperature wise. She addresses the 5th, 6th, and 7th Chakras. She is deeply spiritual, gently helping one to deal with the irritants and inflammatory areas of our spirit, soul and body. The Tiwi people have used KARNTIRRIKANI, their indigenous name for this tree, for thousands of years as an immune stimulant, pain relief (for muscle, bone, and tendon), colon cramps, and antiseptic wash. I use Her a lot for shingles pain in and around the intercostals muscles located in the rib area. In modern tests She has proven to be also very antiviral, aiding insect bites and poison, varicose veins and muscle injuries. Most non-native people, including those who distill Her, do not mention her for use in meditation and ceremony. This does not preclude Her being used extensively by the indigenous just for that. For those who seek out sacred uses of Trees and Plants, or sacred practices period, the ancient way has always been reticent about such so as not to have it desecrated by the opinions of those who do not know anything about it and desire their opinions to rule. The people who deny such have forgotten in their remembrance that, 'THESE ARE ALL MY RELATIONS.' I have been using this incredible essence on others and myself for about five years now. My thoughts conclude with Her truly being a queen who has surfaced again at this special time in Earth History to help bring us home to our inner truths in every dimension.

> *They are beautiful in Their Peace, They are wise in Their silence.*
>
> *They will stand after we are dust. They teach us, and we tend Them.*
>
> -Galeainip Altiem MacDunelmor

VIII. ELEMI

LATIN NAME: CANARIUM LUZONICUM, COMMUNIS

FAMILY NAME: BURSERACEAE

Humans have known this Deva since ancient time, so much so that a lot of written acknowledgement has been created. She has often been called "Poor Man's Frankincense," but thankfully that is just a human statement of illusion, based on the past concerning cost difference and not on True Content, Substance and Perspective of this Deva Herself. STILLNESS, QUIET, PEACE describes Her Angelic qualities.

Elemi mainly comes to us from the forests of the Philippine Islands and has been harvested for eons to facilitate pain relief, glandular harmony, and stimulate the immune system. She is also anti-fungal (try it on fungus that thrives underneath toenails, fingernails) and helps to heal gangrene, ulcers, abscesses, amoebic infections, colitis, and diarrhea. Elemi addresses nervous exhaustion, helps to stop bleeding from fresh cuts and puncture wounds, and helps to tone aged skin and reduce wrinkles. She is also a respiratory queen, addressing bronchitis and relieving coughing. Elemi is full of chemotypes called *sesquiterpenes*. Sesquiterpenes have received a lot of attention in the organic chemistry world because they have been found to heavily interact with human receptor and transmitter sites. This is enough to excite many left-brained humans, stimulating them to believe that just on a one-dimensional level, such chemotypes have incredible abilities with the inner molecules of emotion and many unknown biological interactions with the human body. However, Elemi is a very multi-dimensional being that can facilitate amazing effects on every level of our existence on this plane.

Elemi is a large, unpretentious Tree that produces beautiful white or yellow flowers. She is a tropical, evergreen tree that also produces green fruits, which in turn produces nuts called *pili*. The tree's essence seeps out from Her bark, turning into a yellowish resin or gum (indicated by the name canarium or canary yellow), which is then distilled to obtain the essential essence of Elemi, as we know it. This is basically the same process as for Frankincense and Myrrh. All three of these Devas come from the *Burseraceae* Family. The word Burseraceae means "Dry Fire", which truly depicts Their character. The name Elemi is derived from an Arabic phrase meaning "As above, so below." Her auric colors, according to Medicinal Aromatherapist, Valerie Worwood, (*The Fragrant Heavens*), are bright orange, with a reddish tinge into yellow green. All of this is food for thought when considering Her spiritual and emotional gifts.

She has a joyous, calming, and grounding quality for all who partake of Her. She is centering, quieting your mind so that your Heart can speak to you about what is really going on with you.

She helps you to access your inner feelings, helping you to release deeply held emotions so that you can move through change more easily and in a more balanced way. Elemi empathically encourages you to continue on your path of being the grandest version of the highest expression of who you believe you are without compromise, or betraying yourself in order not to betray another. She does not tell you that God Consciousness is out there beyond reach, BUT WITHIN YOU. You are part and one with all – including Mother Father God Creator. You are a co-creator of your destiny. Elemi will definitely bring your deep hidden emotions to the front room of your house so that you will be able to see and Do your work - If YOU CHOOSE. I think of an old proverb that says, "Without a vision the people perish." Today we see many having visions, visions of war and the like which point to low vibrational energy and shadowy lives. Elemi helps you visualize Divine Love and Peace, which is the Ultimate Vision. Do you resonate with what has been written here? If so, create a relationship with Elemi and you will experience a new friend that will always be there for you.

Happiness is when what you think, what you say, and
What you do are in harmony.
-Mohandas Gandhi

ix. EUCALYPTUS BLUE MALLE

LATIN NAME: EUCALYPTUS POLYBRACTEA

CINEOLE/CRYPTONE

FAMILY NAME: MYRTACEAE

One hardly knows where to start when it comes to this family of Devas. Many humans are aware that the Myrtaceae family are extremely gifted and aid wonderful healing for the body in the area of respiratory illnesses. There are in excess of 40 species known and named by botanists worldwide, however, there are probably more. In the Medicinal Aromatherapy world there are about 16 that have been distilled, at one time or another. At this time, one can readily find about 12 if you know where to look. The art of adulteration is a huge problem with **Eucalyptus** because of the popularity of this essence. There are still many bottles out there that just say Eucalyptus on them, without any notation of the actual botanical name. Be assured that the Eucalytus in these bottles is adulterated! I have chosen to speak here more specifically on a pair of twin sisters that have been located and named, only recently, in relation to the history of Medicinal Aromatherapy. They are Eucalyptus Blue Mallee cineole and cryptone types.

I find it interesting that these were discovered originally as one species. Then, in time, the 'nose' tests were done, and bingo, we come up with a pair of twins! Personally, I believe when you talk with these essences, you will find that they are twins and have characteristics similar to those of human twins. Yes, they both have some of each of the same major chemotypes, just in different ratios. The cineole sister is well known because the chemotype or Deva cineole 1, 8 is very popular among the scientists studying medicinal aromatherapy chemotypes. It is highly effective for all types of bacterial respiratory problems. I invite her in whenever a patient is experiencing the onset of respiratory disease. When I see a patient that has a well-developed case already in motion, such as chronic bronchitis, emphysema or smoker's lung, then I invite both the twins, and especially the cryptone twin to assist. She will address, without question, viral dis- ease and its many side components. Her anti-bacterial action is huge. I have made use of these two, over and over again, with good success. I have not yet seen an article written on these glorious Devas. These two do have other gifts that are well worth mentioning. They have aided in such dis-eases as prostatitis, epididymitis, chlamydia, gonococcus, uterine dysplasia, arthritis, aches and pains, colds, flus, myxovirus, and infections with both positive and negative gram bacteria.

The emotional and spiritual gifts of the twins are likewise similar, as are those on the physiological level. The cineole Deva is more gentle than the cryptone. Nervous exhaustion can be addressed by one or both of them, depending on the condition. Generally, it is the leaves and twigs, which represent the prime area of breathing for these gorgeous trees. "I Am Like The Breath Of Life. I will ignite your passion for emotional and spiritual breath that is smooth, strong, deep, gentle, clean and flowing. I will purify your mind, heart and spirit from the spiritual dust in your spiritual lungs."

She continues, "Have you ever been to a remote mesa, butte, and mountain where silence is so sacred and alive? You can feel it, not fear it, embrace and feel the security of it wrap its loving arms around you. Then you take a deep inhale and breathe in everything you are feeling and not feeling? When I am Pure the above experience is like what you will experience and feel with me! I have spoken!" Welcome to the taste of pure environmental breath, Naturally, Spiritually, and Emotionally.

Let my soul, a shining Tree, silver branches lift towards Thee.

Where on a hallowed winter's night the clear-eyed

Angels May alight.

-Siegfried Sassoon

X. FRANKINCENSE

LATIN NAME: BOSWELLIA CARTERII

FAMILY NAME: BURSERACEAE

Frankincense, *(Boswellia carterii)* yielding Her precious treasure that has been revered for thousands of years, is speaking to me today.[1] She tells me, "I am one of the few essences that you humans have either heard about, talked about, experienced in churches, used in meditations, ceremonies or used on your body for medicinal purposes. I have affected and moved hundreds of millions of your species- physically, emotionally and spiritually, in almost every conceivable way. I have helped change world views, brought spiritual enlightenment, healed cancers, tumors, enhanced love and sexuality beyond many of your wildest dreams. Masking the odor of cremations, consecrating temples, making cosmetics, and treating every conceivable dis-ease from gout to concussions. I have been there for you."

She continues, "In fact, during some of My greatest giving to you, back in the days of Alexandria, a major processing distillation center, Pliny the Elder described a security system as strict as any today, saying,

Good heavens! No vigilance is sufficient to guard the factories... before the workers are allowed to leave the premises, they have to take off all their clothes... My name- Frankincense does reveal my character quite well when you look at me closely. **Frank** gives you the gift of authenticity to look at and go into your own life, and see what is truly going on. **In** is as 'in this life', now, in the moment of your very present feelings and experiences. I am with you to see and **cense**- shower you again with a true sense of You and who You really are."

Frankincense, when it is really pure vs. adulterated in any way, resonates so deeply with our God consciousness. The Masters who have used Her since time began often speak about the calmness and serenity that pervades in Her presence.

The indigenous surroundings of Her homeland cultivate the stamina and sweetness that we so much love about Her. Somalia is one of Her main homes and has a desert climate much like that of Arizona. An extremely hardy species without equal, She has exquisite flower blossoms that create pure white petals, red centers and a green nub in the middle. Her overall aura is Love in the Love Paradigm. You know, there are those of us in the fear paradigm who claim to love but Frankincense knows only Love in Love, just like all of the rest of the Tree and Plant Kingdom.   Some of Her other gifts of helping when it comes to disease are: anti-viral, anti-bacterial, bruises, burns, prostatitis, cancer, Hodgkin's, leukemia, Parkinson's, dementia, MS, leprosy, Alzheimer's, depression, asthenia, ulcers, bronchitis, asthma. She stimulates and strengthens. If you believe that you do not know Her, think again... She's influenced your very DNA. Her warmth is worldwide.

Trees are the Earth's endless effort to Speak to the listening Heaven.

-Rabindranath Tagor

---

[1] There are other sub-species by other Latin names, but this one is of the oldest and the most famous. We consistently find the resonance with Her, over and above, the others. This does not negate the others.

XI. GOLDENROD

LATIN NAME: SOLIDAGO CANDENSIS

FAMILY NAME: ASTERACEAE

UH-OH!!!... OH NO!!! Do not even tell me that Barry is going to consider **Goldenrod**, *(Solidago Canadensis)*, viable for medicinal aromatherapy use. Absolutely, I am. She is an ancient Native American Herb and Essence that is returning to us to facilitate the healing of all types of heart dis-eases. The Latin name *Solidago* means, "To Make Whole". There are over 75 species in the U.S. alone and those distilling Her live in Canada. Can you imagine telling some people about the beauty and amazing properties of this much maligned plant here in the U.S.? The Plants & Trees are constantly being blamed for almost every allergy problem that arises. How many times have you heard Goldenrod being mentioned as a prime suspect? I will leave the allergy illusionists to their own endless circular searches and move on. The Trees & Plants have been around way before Humans, and I suggest that we should start re-evaluating the true origin of the allergy monster.

Goldenrod *(Solidgao canadensis)*, is from the Asteraceae family of plants and is considered in Botany to be of the highest evolvement. She involves one major stalk of life and energy, plus a whole collective consciousness of flowers grouped together on top. They are showing the world that YES we can live together in love and harmony, no matter what.

This Deva has a large percentage of monoterpenes like apinene, myrcene, limonene; sesquiterpenes like germacrene-D; and esters like bornyl acetate and alcohols like borneol and methyl chavicol. Goldenrod stimulates the liver cells and bladder cells in eliminating toxins and poisoning. She is especially known for facilitating healing for pericarditis, hypertension, endocarditis, arteritis, disharmonized blood pressure, neurasthenia, and spasmohilia. She can stimulate the calming of a nervous stomach. I find Her to be quite helpful when working with the solar plexus and cardiac inflammation. Used in synergistic togetherness with Ylang Ylang complete (Canaga odorata), Cardamon Seed Green (Elettaria cardamomun). Cardamom Seed Black (Amomum subulatum), Inula graveolens, as a heart tonic, Goldenrod is beautifully effective.

As I am continuing to use Her more on the spiritual and emotional issues of life, I find Her very opening and nurturing, to the 4th charka. She has an amazing ability to captivate your attention very quickly with Her strength of character, bringing to mind heart issues of great importance, however painful, to surface with ease, softness and empathy. You will see those heart issues through not only your eyes, but also Her eyes, which will bring new light, information and restfulness to your heart. With Her heart and yours meshed together, a new prism of possibilities will emerge for your glorious consideration.

And in addition to all of the above benefits described you can even seriously consider Her for HAY FEVER, SINUS INFEC-TIONS, ALLERGIES AND CONGESTION. Consider this Deva to be a gift, and She will show you truths that will allow you to laugh, cry and smile.

Happiness is a wind of the rarest vintage.
-Logan Pearsall Smith

XII. GUAIACWOOD

LATIN NAME: GUAIACUM O. LIGUM SANCTUM

FAMILY NAME: ZYGOPHYLLACEAE

This mysterious enchantress, *Guaiacum officinalis*, is one of the most elusive, non-conforming essences in all of Medicinal Aromatherapy. Through literature in Spanish and English, we glean the amazing stories that come down through the corridors of time about this Deva. The Spaniards came to the West, finding many humans who were much happier, healthier and cleaner than they themselves. These precious natives of the Americas and Islands helped the Spaniards' heal many of their sicknesses with **Guaiacwood**. The Spaniards' lifestyle was quite unhealthy on many levels. The unfamiliarity and new acquaintance with the Spaniards caused the native people to become desperately ill from contact with such filthy specimens of our race. Then instead of thanking the natives for the care and wisdom of healing they gave them, the Spaniards commenced to kill them. Queen Guaiacwood has seen it all. Even today, She speaks mightily of Her love for balance, and reaches out to us to help heal our abuses, which afflict so many. She asks once again, "How LONG will it be until we truly desire to create new stories of love, peace and happiness? How much is our misery really worth to us? Is experiencing pain, guilt, shame, and regret really your desire?"

A student of ours recently channeled a message from Guaiac-wood. Here is a part of it: "I am standard-bearer for our tropics, and have endured many intrusions into our healing lands by you humans. We are honor bound to give you the healing properties we possess, but you never give back anything to us. Therefore your world is out of balance, and will continue to be more so until you can understand that we DESERVE better than what you have given us, which is nothing. We respond to you, if you can conceive of such a thing, as interacting with a Tree or Plant. Try it. Our world will become more hellish until you do so. We were all put here together, and we are not less than you, although that is difficult for the human ego to contain. I am liver cleansing, anti-viral and anti-bacterial. The spleen can also be positively affected, increasing leucocyte activity in dangerous dis-eases, the number and severity of which you are just starting to see. Apply me directly to the liver and spleen areas three times a day for maximum effect in dis-ease states."[1]

Other medicinal uses are anti-aging (She tightens loose skin), Herpes 1 and 2, boils, acne, sores, moon pain, frigidity, impotence, water retention, genital and urinary infections, inflammation of joints, muscles, glands, and blemishes. Shamanically, She calls forth unfocused souls to regain their concentration in their journeys here on Earth Mother.

And in a most gentle, subtle way, Guaiacwood soothes feelings of LOSS on all levels of our lives. Many people fail to remember all the many areas this touches. In ancient times, She was used in embalming, preserving the body while also alleviating the feelings of grief of those preparing the body (often, the family). Recently someone called me saying they had knee replacement surgery on both knees. They went on telling me how sad they were feeling and wondered what the cause could be? They still had pain, but could walk, and overall their life was getting back to normal. The sadness was a mystery. Their body had experienced a loss of two knee parts, which no doubt were thrown into medical waste, burned, etc., with never a thought of remembrance from the soul and spirit of this person that the body could be in pain and sadness from that loss.

My dear ones, even in surgery when we permit our bodies to undergo cutting and removal, (especially internally), try to remember the angst your own beautiful body goes through for you. Guaiacwood has opened Herself to be there for you for such an experience. It is really no different from what amputees go through. May I suggest a ceremony for lost body parts. Every atom of our makeup has the name of Creator on it. Guaiacwood calls forth love, remembrance, and gentleness for which all levels of our existence longs for... honoring, tender loving care and acknowledgment that I do indeed have worth.

God is the experience of looking at a Tree and saying, "AH"
-Joseph Campbell

---

[1] Thanks (K. Taylor), one of our students.

XIII. HYSSOP

LATIN NAME: HYSSOP OFFICINALIS

FAMILY NAME: LAMIACEAE

Here is a Deva that has so much to offer in our day of violence, hatred and anger. She is all about FORGIVENESS and clearing guilt and resentment from our lives. Anyone who has read any Hebrew, Islamic or Christian writings, will find mention of this most revered Plant. In Exodus 12:22, you will find the famous statement about using **Hyssop** with Lambs blood for protection against the death of the first born during the tenth plague. This meant that those families that applied it on their doorposts and lintels were forgiven, or literally not given the sentence or judgment of the killing of their first born of the household. You will also find Her mentioned in various Islamic and Christian writings. Hyssop has an amazing gift for working in the central nervous system stimulating the neurotransmitters and receptors into action. Actually, as do all essences, She works first with the spiritual, then the emotional, then outwardly to the physical. We have had many of our clients and students call us to tell us about their experiences in this area of forgiveness over the years. She will bring up our "stuff" fast for our consideration in hopes that we will work on it and create a wonderful new story.

Also, She is capable of aiding in the following ways: She is anti-viral, famous in the Middle East for Her help with HIV, Hepatitis ABCD. She helps to equalize cardiac stress, being a significant blood purifier, blood pressure balancer, and healer of sore throats. Organic chemists have found that the leaves hold antiseptic and anti-viral properties in Her essence sacs. Even the outside leaves have been found to produce a mold that produces penicillin.

There has been, in the past years, a lot of talk in some circles about the dangers of this Deva, as well as those of many others. (Refer to my twelve points) Just know that when you apply the suggested amounts topically, there is no danger, just help. Again, this book is not about Fear but Divine Love, using Wisdom, Knowledge, Experience, Feelings and Common Sense. When in doubt, seek out a Medicinal Aromatherapist that works from a paradigm of Divine Love. If our traditional Allopathic followers would do this, the mortality rate of people passing over would be very different.

I would like to share with you some findings from various case studies over the years regarding *Hyssop Officinalis*. I am not in the habit of doing this, but I desire that you view just one scientific attempt with their frame of reference, to show admission to the importance of the Plant and Tree Kingdom.

Research Paper Case History: Inhibition of HIV replication by Hyssop Officinalis extracts by Kreis W Kaplan MH Freeman J Sun DK Sarin PS Anti viral Res (1990 Dec) 14 (6):323-37. I am condensing this study for the purpose mentioned above.

"Crude extracts of dried leaves of Hyssop Officinalis showed strong anti-HIV activity as measured by inhibition of syncytia formation, HIV reverse transcriptase (RT), and p. 17 and p. 24 antigen expression, but were non-toxic to the uninfected Molt-3 cells. Commercial caffeic acid showed good antiviral activity in the RT assay and high to moderate activity in the syncytia assay and the p17 and p24 antigen expression. Tannic acid and gallic acid, common to other teas, could not be identified in our extracts. When commercial products of these two acids were tested in our assay systems, they showed high to moderate activity against HIV-1. **HYSSOP OFFICINALIS EXTRACTS CONTAIN CAFFEIC ACID, UNIDENTIFIED TANNINS, AND POSSIBLY A THIRD CLASS OF UNIDENTIFIED HIGHER MOLECULAR WEIGHT COMPOUNDS THAT EXHIBIT STRONG ANTI- HIV ACTIVITY, AND MAY BE USEFUL IN THE TREATMENT OF PATIENTS WITH AIDS.**

The investigation into Hyssop's anti-AIDS properties began after a 29-year-old female heroin addict suffering from the virus arrived for treatment at North Shore University Hospital in Manhassett, New York. In addition to other ailments she had at the time, the woman had contracted Kaposi's sarcoma, a deadly cancer characterized by the bluish red lesions that frequently develop in people who have AIDS.

A year later, a checkup revealed that the woman's skin lesions had improved "significantly" and she was feeling "much better". The source of her improvement was a mystery, until the woman's mother told researchers that her daughter had been drinking an old Jamaican tea remedy made from Hyssop and a few other herbs. What were the doctors to think? They weren't used to see-ing Kaposi's sarcoma get better. In fact, until the time of her death from AIDS related pneumonia, the woman continue to drink her tea, and her Kaposi's sarcoma continued to regress. "After we heard that, we decided to study Hyssop," says Dr. Willi Kreis, M.D., PhD, an oncologist at North Shore University Hos-pital and research professor at Cornell Medical College in New York City. "The team's lab work, chronicled in a leading medical journal, seems to confirm Hyssop's preliminary promise," says Dr. Kreis. "Our study was done just with tissue cultures in the labo-ratory, but Hyssop was very effective as an antiviral, anti HIV treatment in the test system that we used."

Thank you, Hyssop. What a beautiful healing robe of lavender purple you are every time you blossom.

Purge me with Hyssop till I am pure;
Wash me till I am whiter than snow;
-Psalm 51:9, Melek David (Tanakh)

XIV. IMMORTELLE EVERLASTING

LATIN NAME: HELICHRYSUM ITALICUM,

ARENARIUM

FAMILY NAME: ASTERACEAE

The botanical name, *Helichrysum*, is derived from the Greek "Helios," meaning sun, and "Chrysos," meaning gold. She was popularized in the U.S. by Pierre Franchomme and Daniel Penoel, M.D." After having explored with many types of "everlasting" oils, one variety, *helichrysum italicum sp. serotinum corsician*, that originates from the Island of Corsica, was found to have extraordinary healing qualities." She is more anti-inflammatory than Blue Chamomile, and more tissue regenerating than Lavender. As a cicatrizant (aiding in the formation of scar tissue), She compares with Cistus. Her effects are so convincing that She has never met with any kind of criticism, despite the absence of scientific data on Her effectiveness. Helichrysum essence demonstrates that anecdotal evidence can create a reality without the help of industrially sponsored science. Her proven "graces" are mind-boggling.

I would also like to introduce the sub-species *arenarium*, that we find to be equal to the italicum in every way except in energetic personality, which would be natural. She is a bit more gentle and smooth than her twin sister italicum. I have personally used it myself many times with Italicum and find Them to be beyond amazing together. Recently, I had an occasion to use Arenarium on myself due to an injury and I found I could use Her even a bit sooner on an open wound than italicum, if I were to rate the amount of sting created by one or the other.

We are so thankful to find this other **immortelle** and **everlasting**, because italicum is having a difficult time due to climate changes and all that comes with that. The price is soaring yet arenarium is not far behind. Mother knows how to take care of us and the Plants and Trees are coming to our rescue. Here are some of the glorious attributes of these two Devas:

• **General Medicinal Properties:** *anti-allergenic, anti-spasmodic, anti-inflammatory, anti-viral, anti-bacterial, anti-microbial, anti-tussive (relieves coughs), antiseptic, astringent, anti-bruising, expectorant, fungicidal, diuretic, hepatic, nervine and cholesterol (balancing).*

• **General Digestive System:** *liver and spleen congestion, viral colitis, gallbladder infections, pancreatic stimulant, stomach cramps.*

• **Respiratory system:** *asthma, chronic bronchitis, chronic coughs, flu, colds, whooping cough.*

• **Hormonal System:** *Emotions, nervous system. depression, nervous exhaustion, neuralgia, grief, panic, addiction detox (physical and mental).*

• **Wounds & scar tissue:** *Essence of choice for healing scar tissue (recent or previous), stops bleeding, helps a scab form and tissue to repair itself. Use with Cistus steam distilled or absolute. With nut oil such as Rose Hip Seed (rosa rubiginosa), minimizes stretch marks, acne scars, and surgical scars.*

• **Skin Dis-Harmony:** *bruises, abscesses, chronic dermatitis, rosacea, eczema, psoriasis, stretch marks, sore nipples, cracked or itchy skin, varicose veins, sunburn, warts, athlete's foot, boils and burns.*

• **Spiritual growth:** *Helichrysum's ability to heal emotional scarring, enhance the flow of subtle heart energy and connect the body with spirit makes it an invaluable aid in spiritual growth. Helps visualization, personal growth and compassion. In addition, Their vibratory frequencies are extremely high, which allows access to higher levels of consciousness.*

• **Helichrysum italicum sp. serotinum Corsican and sp. arenarium:** *are true gifts, unique in Their extreme broad spectrum possibilities.*

Flowers are love's truest language.
-Park Benjamin

xv. ANGEL INULA GRAVEOLENS

LATIN NAME: INULA GRAVEOLENS

FAMILY NAME: ASTERACEAE

By far one of the most amazing essences being distilled in small amounts, *Inula gravelolens*, from the Asteraceae family, has almost no information written about Her in this country, except perhaps a physical description and identification of Her chemotypes.

With a chronological birthday recently revealing that I have now entered the "60 zone," I have explored this Deva extensively on my own precious physical heart. My heart still sees me through 12-14 hour days, doing all the things that most of you know about me. About ten drops of Inula graveolens applied topically warms my chest, and penetrates deeply so quickly that I can feel Her nurturing and cuddling my heart in minutes. She has been known from ancient times to be a heart regulator for rhythm. She facilitates strengthening the heart muscle, toning it and the aorta and coronary vessels. That being said, She aids in preventing tachycardia and inflammation of the heart. In times like these, this Deva is giving of Herself freely for us. Heart issues have always been important and crucial in every age of this planet, but at this time, with the shift upon us, They are even more so. What a gift She is! And the list of Her gifts goes on.

A member of the **Sunflower** Family, Inula graveolens (or odorata), does not have a common or colloquial name, just the botanical name above. Organic chemists say that She contains sesquiterpenes, which has been very exciting to them because they feel that these chemotypes aid such conditions as poor immunity, immune dis-eases and cancers like leukemia.

Another area that I have experienced extensively with clients, and myself, is the anti histamine gifts that She has. Just one drop on the nose and one drop in the nose opens up all the nasal passages and stops sneezing and itching. Mucous drainage, allergies, asthma, acute and chronic bronchitis, rhinopharyngitis, tonsil/trachea inflammation and irritating coughs are definitely within Her range of expertise. Trying to eat well in this country is not always easy, and there are times when I can get mucous drainage very quickly from what I've eaten. Applying Her topically on the area of concern as soon as possible stops it for me within 15 minutes.

Inula is also amazing for skin problems such as fungi, strange rashes, herpes, and dermatitis. The digestive tract likes Her for liver worms (flukes, facida hepatica, tape worms), because these worms do not desire to stay around long when She comes to say, "Hi!"

All in all, She has shown me over and over again how softly courageous Her personality truly is. Her life force is so strong, Her help so powerful, Her action so rapid. At this time, because

She is hard to find, She is expensive, yet is available to those She is calling to.

Shining forth like dew drops from Father Sun
The Blossoms of Inula speak loud.
In You Creator my Heart rejoices in a Chorus of Hallelujah.
-B. B. Kapp

XVI. JUNIPER BRANCH
JUNIPER WITH THE BERRY
JUNIPER BERRY ONLY

LATIN NAME: JUNIPERUS COMMUNIS

FAMILY NAME: CUPRESSACEAE

A close sister to Cypress, **Juniper/Juniper Berry** is an unparalleled essence, with an ability to use every part of the tree-bark, root, leaves and berries. Some write that the bark or wood alone, without the berry, is not very therapeutic; however, this is not really true. Many times, different parts of a plant or tree are yet to be distilled and explored by practitioners and users, because we have no modern frame of reference from which to pull from. Both the branches and berries together or separate provide therapeutic value. I do have a small farmer that has distilled a small amount of Juniper berries only and was just fantastic. There are now a few full time farmers doing Juniper berry alone and this too is absolutely wonderful. The price is higher yet well worth the purchase. If you live where Juniper berry lives, try harvesting only berries and observe how long it takes to harvest a five-gallon bucket full. Therapeutically the intensity of the berries only would be greater. Every part of the Tree has specific essence sacs unique to itself. Every part of a Tree or Plant is precious.

Juniper's ancient wisdom is still witnessed in the Southwest with grandmother Junipers reaching ages of over 2,000-years-old (even in my area, although these are not distilled at present, but are close relatives). I find Her to be one of the most outgoing Tree Friends we have. She is easy to talk to and receive from.

Juniper berry addresses memory also. In combination with Rosemary, She works wonders with failing short-term memory. She is also famous in the diuretic department, stimulating digestion, metabolism, kidney functioning and the like. The American Zuni women drank the tea to relax their muscles after delivering their babies. The Kwakiutis used Her for shortness of breath. The Cree used Her for all sorts of external skin dis-eases, including weeping eczema, acne, wounds and for managing digestive and mange ailments with their dogs.

Juniperus communis works as an overall balancer and cleanser of the CNS, the renal system, and digestive system. Valnet writes that, "Juniper essence even imparts a scent of violets to urine." I use it in my practice constantly as well as on my own body, to balance and stimulate faster harmony for sluggish digestion. Juniperus communis and Sandalwood (Santalum album, spicatum), are wonderful cleansers for many genital-urinary dis-harmonies. I take Her internally as an antiseptic and blood purifier. Helping to rid oneself of uric acid is one of Her specialties. Externally, I use it on my patients to promote excretion of uric acid, which helps individuals suffering from all types of gout. I have used Her extensively on patients for a heart balancer, knowing that She also addresses blood purification along the way. She is a spiritual blood cleanser and purifier without equal. The life is in the blood, so as an example, if you have believed that you have become a victim and you have given your power away in one way or another, Juniper Berry will come to your aid and ask you if you would desire to create a new story about the situation you find yourself in. She opens the way to new beginnings with gentleness and easy flow.

She can also be used for prostatitis, applied to the perineum 5-10 drops daily. When you use Her with *Santalum album* or *spicatum, Abies balsamea*, or *Hypericum perforatum millepertius* you can expect results. Juniperus communis is an anti-diabetic, having as one of its major constituents, sugar. The sugar content can be as high as 73%. When I treat animals for various types of mange, She definitely facilitates healing. I layer Rosemarius officinalis with Juniperus communis for the same problems. Some people chat about not using Her at all when one knows that their kidneys have an acute inflammation. At this point of my exploration with this beautiful Angel, I am not worried about such. Jean Valnet, the famous French MD Medicinal Aromatherapist, and others talk about using it for urinary stones. Could She be used for kidney stones that manifest and reveal dis-harmony? Case histories and empirical experiences are what we must have, before saying 'no' to this and 'no' to that usage of essential essences. So much fear is wrapped around the human being and that fear literally extinguishes life every day with drugs from the drug companies, yet we willingly and even stupidly stereotype this (fear) concept over to Mother Earth and Plant and Tree Kingdoms which knows how to harmonize chemicals.

Juniperus communis can be taken internally as well as externally, inhaled, etc. Remember, external use outweighs, in most cases, internal use because of dilution from digestive juices.

As a nervine, Juniperus communis is marvelous, second to none. It should be used for depression, apathy, confusion, anxiety, and paranoia. Emotional dis-eases of anxiety, fear, negative energy, abandonment, energy holes and lack of purpose and direction can be helped and addressed in amazing ways with this Queen. She comes to the rescue in a miraculous way in stimulating nerve tissue regeneration from injuries of all kinds. She is refreshing and helps one stay in a meditative frame of mind throughout the day. She definitely is a love frequency booster! She is YIN (Temperature)/YIN (Energy) in nature, wooing everyone in the most Angelic way. In Her own unique manner, She is a Messenger of Love, bringing hope and joy where there has been only shame, regret and guilt. She will help shame turn into..." I am good and very special;" regret turns into..." all things work together for the good of me," guilt turns into..." I finally have my power back and I can get on with my life." In a word... she brings PERSPECTIVE.

Juniperus communis has a personality that is strongly revealed when eating her seeds. I recommend sitting down in a lotus position and feasting on them in a meditative state. Your experience will begin. In our new yard in the Sedona area, we have many Juniperus communis trees, young and old. One young one revealed Her name as Helia and She was so excited to have us come and be with them. What a conversation I had with Her. Words cannot express the feelings when we start to communicate with such dear, wise, gentle, and precious friends. She is here to offer Herself to you– will you take the time to learn from Her?

I am the heat of your hearth, the shade screening you from the sun;

I am the beam that holds your house, the board of your table;

I am the handle of your hoe, the door of your homestead; the wood of your cradle, and the shell of your coffin.

I am the gift of God and the friend of man.

-Author Unknown

xvii. LAUREL LEAF

LATIN NAME: **LAURUS NOBILIS**

FAMILY NAME: **LAURACEAE**

The nobility of *Laurus nobilis*, **(Laurel Leaf)**, has been announced throughout history. Even the family name, Lauraceae, bespeaks this Queen. This family includes Anise Raven, Cassia Bark, Cinnamon Bark, Cinnamon Leaf, Ravensara, Rosewood and Rhododendron. As prestigious a list as this comprises, Laurus nobilis yet stands in a category all her own.

As an essential essence, *Laurus nobilis* is steam distilled from the chopped up, leafy branches in order for the distillation process to produce the greatest yield possible. The essence of Laurus nobilis matures and gets even stronger, more graceful, and deeper over time. This is actually true of all pure essences So be patient with Her, and She will bless you as time moves forward.

Laurus nobilis is considered one of the foremost Queens for the body's lymphatic system. Whenever I sense a problem of degeneration with a patient, I will use Her immediately, with confidence and great admiration for Her abilities, which are without equal. She is very Yin in temperature and Yin energetically. You can apply Her neat over the heart area, 10-15 drops every morning before showering, and experience an incredible aura of protection around you for the forthcoming day. She is a continuous catalyst for our immune system. Emotionally, She stimulates the molecules of nobility, sense of well-being, heroism, fortitude, courage and stalwartness. She announces the goddess and god in each of us, and encourages us to come out of our closets, wooing us to happily walk our journey here in this dimension. "Do not shrink back," She often tells me. "I will wash you with My in-depth aromas; fill you on a molecular level with courage, and commune with your molecules as family. We will talk, share and be in a good place because, as in all things, we are one."

Laurus nobilis will address digestion, lack of alertness, is anti-viral, a wonderful tonic for kidneys and reproductive organs, stimulates alertness, and addresses hypotension. Laurel Leaf addresses Lyme dis-ease, which is a virus not common to the human. Our immune system must identify and go through molecular procedures to stalk out and build defenses against these foreign molecules. The molecules of Laurel Leaf and our own bodies will commune together and discuss with the Lyme molecules, come to an agreement, and send the Lyme molecules back to a better place than the human body.

Laurus nobilis has ester chemotypes or Devas in Her that also are wonderfully antispasmodic. She has large portions of cineol, linalool and methyl eugenol to name a few.

With Earth Changes and Human Dysfunctional Repetitive Behavior increasing, She speaks loudly: "REMEMBER ME."

SHE SPEAKS, "I am an ancient one like all of my sisters. I

walked ahead and planted myself as the human migrations took place over earth. I desired to be there for you in times of great sorrow, transition, new journeys, and new dreams. I've given courage for those who were in fear and calmness for those who were full of anxiety. I've been there for you when you were sick and desired hot broth from my leaves with all of the energy to quickly aid your immune system to bounce back. Today, I desire to say once again, 'YOU ARE LOVED.' With many new maladies coming your way, many from your own doings, I can be of help: with cancer, Lyme Dis-ease, the scary new Morgollon Dis-ease, lupus, hormonal problems, kidney problems, West Nile virus, and the Avian Flu. Your animals and pets love me for many of the same purposes. The more you domesticate your animal friends, the more they become like you."

"If you apply 10-15 drops, I will put an aura of protection around you for the day. Every being on Earth Mother is being pelted with toxic darts of all kinds. The many fumes from all of your air travel are adding fuel to the fire. Chemtrails is another huge problem. My advice is to stop arguing and know the pollution is massive and sickness is increasing just from that alone. I work well with many of my sisters— Eucalyptus family, Rosemary family, Conifer family, Frankincense, Lavender Family, Basil family, and many others. I support all attempts for detox which I would encourage you to take seriously because all of you are on overload. Even we of the Tree and Plant Kingdom feel it and are sadly suffering. If things really got tough and I was the only one that you could take with you, you would be blessed."

Laurel Leaf has been successful for so many of our clients, friends and family that we could, literally write pages. To experience Her directly, to feel Her working, will always be the best Teacher. This is an essence from which you could benefit from by taking Her with you at all times just to sniff. An example of this is when one of our clients is on the subway or in a huge traffic jam; after one or two sniffs, the congestion and intensity (not to mention the toxicity of the pollution) is greatly reduced.

Laurus nobilis can reveal to us that which is hidden. In Greece, they compared Her to the Sun, which is the eye of God, who sees all and helps us to see. The Roman conquerors were honored by laurel branches when coming home from battle. The Caesars were crowned with Her. Permit Laurel Leaf to be one of your mentors.

We belong to no cult. We are not nature lovers.

We don't love nature any more than we love breathing.

Nature is simply something indispensable, like

air and light and water,that we accept as necessary

to living.

And the nearer we can get to it the happier we are.

-Louise Dickenson Rich

XVIII. LIME, MEXICAN

LATIN NAME: CITRUS AURANTIFOLIA

FAMILY NAME: RUTACEAE

Lime, Mexican packs a punch even a little bit more than Lemon, Cedro when it comes to boosting the pH up over 7.2. For many years I have used Her for helping individuals change from an acidic pH to an alkaline pH. It just seems like without an alkaline pH, no matter what we do, the body just balks at facilitating healing. In other words, our body likes to have an alkaline pH before it willingly goes to work to heal Itself. I cannot tell you how many times I have seen this to be true. Clients come to me saying how they have tried this and that, spent thousands of dollars to no avail. The very first thing I will ask them is if they know what their pH is, and if they have checked it lately? Of course not, their primary physician did not mentioned this to them. Folks, without a correct pH, no medicine of any kind works well, including essential essences. When you juice a lime or lemon once a day or use the pure essence in a glass of water (3-12 drops in a liter to a liter and one half), the acid from the lime or lemon juice converts into carbonates and bicarbonates to create alkalinity. It's like magic every time. Some people just naturally have a good alkalinity, but many are naturally acidic. Also, the way we eat and live has so much to do with this. It is directly related to our immune system or often we say, "our sense of well being".

Another important area that we use Lime, Mexican for is for all levels of cancer. The limonene has become very exciting for organic chemists in the past 15 years due to many of their studies, especially in other countries. The ancients were aware of this very much around the Mediterranean countries. Citrus has been used extensively for eons. In fact, the Mediterranean area is known as the birthplace of the seeding of many Trees and Plants that then migrated across the Earth.

We find mental clarity to be much enhanced when using Lime, Mexican on a regular basis. Other uses are for all addictive behaviors including anorexia, bulimia, alcohol abuse, smoking and drugs. She brings that crisp clear feeling that even helps lift depression, relieve jet lag, and the feelings of loss.

Some might ask, why Lime from Mexico? Because through the years of all the samples that I have tested, She just happens to resonate the most deeply and broadly every time. May you be blessed as you experience Her. We have over 12 years of experience with Her and we never tire of the sweetness that She brings.

Every Tree near our house had a name of its own and a special identity.

This was the beginning of my love for natural things, for Earth and Sky.

For roads and fields and woods, for Trees and Grass and Flowers;

A love that has been second only to my sense of enduring kinship with Birds and Animals, and all inarticulate creatures.

-Ellen Glasgow (1845-1945)

xix. Manuka

LATIN NAME: LEPTOSPERMUM SCOPARIUM

FAMILY NAME: MYRTACEAE

This Deva has been used for thousands of years by the indigenous peoples of New Zealand. She has been steam distilled by the Maori and Waitaha people. She is a bushy plant with long branches and small spiky leaves with pink or white flowers; She has a shrub-like appearance. She also has a unique ability to fill in areas of soil where other species have left, aiding in stabilizing those areas in a wonderful way. Spiritually, She will do the same. When baggage or entities leave a body, using Manuka on the heart or solar plexus helps to protect the individual, until love and warmness begin to fill those empty areas. In fact, Her love will be a part of that filling.

On another level, are you aware that within the underground root systems of the Trees, Shrubs and Plants, there is a sharing of needed nutrients, etc.– not only between the same species, but among different species as well? Love! Manuka has been used continuously as an anti-acne, anti-allergenic, anti-bacterial, anti-fungi, anti-inflammatory and anti-histamine. Today, She is becoming more and more known as our brothers and sisters in New Zealand harvest and distill this most treasured shrub.

By the way, what is the difference between a Plant, Shrub or Tree? They tell me that, just as humans have auras and every level is important; so these three types of Devas live, function and facilitate important duties in the three depths of Earth Mother's immediate aura closest to Her very being. So *Leptospermum scoparium* has an extremely important role to play in helping to harmonize the bacteria, fungi and toxins that live around us, in us, and in other species.

Manuka has, in modern times, been tested on numerous undesirable organisms (molecules) to help determine Her effectiveness in neutralizing dis-ease. Beings that will run from Manuka include staphylococcus, aureus, pyogenes, streptococcus, faecalis, E-coli, candida albicans, apergillus niger, tricholphyton mentagrophytes, bacteria, (both gram + and gram −), yeast, fungi and many others. This wild Deva is also very emotionally and spiritually calming, blanketing our auras with a Mothering Protection in such a gentle way. She has a Yin/Yin personality, with fluid results which are smooth and great. At one stage of Her maturity you will notice the blossoms have a pink center and are white color on the outside. This often denotes pure passion surrounded by the pure white light from Creator. There are many Plants, Shrubs and Trees that have a spiky, strong nature outside, but are oh, so soft, and beautiful as you walk through the outside doors into the deeper secrets of Their being. The fruit of Leptospermum scoparium is also very interesting. Once the blossoms leave, the fruit becomes very visible and looks like a tear drop dipped in chocolate?. In all species there is an ability to be playful and joy-ful in Their unconditional love. This is another Deva with whom to experience a relationship.

> *In all things of nature there is something marvelous.*
> -Aristotole

xx. *Mugwort* WHITE ARMOISE

LATIN NAME: ARTEMISIA HERBA ALBA

FAMILY NAME: MYRTACEAE

Ah-h-h...to be able to move blocked energy in one's body, no matter what level you are focusing on to work through and move forward, feels so good.

Welcome to the world of **Mugwort** from Morocco, hand-picked from the foothills of the Atlas Mountains. This is not the Artemisia vulgaris coming out of China, from which 'moxa' is made. Personalities of the Tree and Plant Kingdoms are as varied and broad as are those of humans. *Artemisia herba alba* has been known among Western European Aromatherapists also as **AR-MOISE, WHITE**. I find this most appropriate, because one of Her greatest gifts is to bestow white light energy around us as a protective shield while we are working on our "stuff" spiritually and emotionally. She directs that energy ultimately into our inner heart core so if we choose, we can create new stories very quickly and disband the old stories that no longer serve us.

I have witnessed Mugwort move stuck energy in seconds, minutes or over several hours, giving wonderful relief to the physical, emotional and spiritual bodies. We as humans so often do not really recognize, or pay attention to ourselves, or our bodies until we get huge pain in a particular place of our anatomy. This situation often brings about a blindness to, and lack of awareness of, the more important issues of the emotional and spiritual areas that are not being addressed. Understandably, there can also be acute accidental circumstances, such as cutting oneself, a motor vehicle accident, etc., that cause physical blockages. We should not forget that all things happening are linked together on some level and fashion- spiritually, emotionally and physically. This process is called "OUR JOURNEY" and our challenge to remember the pieces of the puzzle, poco y poco, a little here and a little there. Why? So that every day, we can be the grandest version of the highest expression of who we believe we truly are.

Mugwort, therefore, is famous on the physical level for working with spasms, sore muscles, pulled muscles, sprains, torn muscles, ligament lesions. She is within a group of Plants that has received the nickname 'Wormwood', which corresponds to Their ability to rid oneself of both physical and spiritual worms. The vibratory frequency of Mugwort is such that physical worms cannot stand to remain in the vicinity of Mugwort, and similarly, spiritual worms desire to flee when the correct work is accomplished in the person's spiritual life. Mugwort has great power to address both upper and lower respiratory dis-eases of all kinds. This again relates to Her ability to eliminate blockages on all levels where

breathing one's life force takes place 24/7. She also helps to harmonize the feminine cycle from moon to moon, bringing peace.
Even the feminine nature in males can be harmonized more readily when Mugwort is around in their lives.

All the cautions about one of her ingredients, *thujone*, raised by
left-brained aromatherapists, who work from a paradigm of fear,
need not steer you away from Mugwort. If you use 5 to 10 drops
a day, depending on weight, age, condition, etc., you can achieve
good results in a short time. Some conditions may call for more
drops. Consult a Medicinal Aromatherapist who works from a
paradigm of love and they will suggest to you a good path.

Lastly, She works with skin issues, helping to regenerate the
largest organ of the body after dis-ease or trauma. All in all,
Mugwort is a Deva that is helping many in the times in which
we are living. She is a great ally as we awaken and come back to
the love paradigm.

Perfumes are the feelings of Flowers.
-Heinrich Heine

XXI. NUTMEG

LATIN NAME: MYRISTICA FRAGRANS

FAMILY NAME: MYRISTICACEAE

Nutmeg *(Myristica fragrans)* seeds, kernels or little nuts are steam-distilled. She is a Tree that grows up to around 45-ft. tall, and can take 30 years to mature. There are both Female and Male Trees. Nutmeg has been famous for millennia in India, Java, Moluccas, Sri Lanka and Sumatra. Interestingly enough, the West has often put out great cautionary signs regarding the use of this precious and many dimensional friend to Humans. Jean Valnet, MD. suggested that over 7-12 mls., (more than 210 drops undiluted), which is a lot, could be toxic. I would agree with Valnet. Yet, people in countries such as India (home to over a billion people) have used Her regularly since ancient times, respecting Her, as all people should. So, as in all things, use wisdom, but do not exclude this powerhouse from your portfolio of essences.

Myristica fragrans exemplifies a huge Life Force that is found in kernels, (not unlike many other Trees or Plants that produce seeds, kernels, etc). I refer to Her as a 'chi warmer' for She has an explicit warming effect as soon as one applies Her on the skin. Applying 10-20 drops on the abdomen, between the bottom of the rib cage down to the pubic bone, helps harmonize cold Chi. The stomach loves Her help in a myriad of problems including vomiting, internal parasites, fermentation, infections and low metabolism. She is a famous helper for general asthenia, (overall physical weakness), facilitating energy and stimulation for the brain, and a strong psycho-stimulant, invigorating, even promoting vivid color dreams. Nutmeg is an overall heart tonic. Since antiquity, She has shown Herself strong as a multi-dimensional aphrodisiac, both emotional and hormonal, balancing estrogen ratios, as well as, progesterone and testosterone. Also on the hormonal front, Nutmeg is used for pelvic pain syndrome, endometriosis, menopause, dysmenorrhea, PMS, and female infertility. She facilitates birthing by easing labor pains and strengthening, toning the muscles used in delivery. She is also very uplifting after birth.

Skin parasites definitely do not like Her at all. She works with gout and all types of muscular and skeletal pains and spasms, by warming everything with which She comes in contact with. Intercostal pain from strained coughing, shingles and pulled intercostals muscles subsides quite readily. I have used Nutmeg for many of the ailments mentioned above. Thinking of spiritual constipation, frigidity, Nutmeg has shown to be wonderful in opening blockages that have stagnated for years. She works on the doors of denial by greasing the doors that finally swing open and LIGHT can come in. She truly is a Deva of Fire, ready to facilitate the burning away of the dross of one's life, if we are ready.

It was not that the jagged precipices were lofty,
that the encircling

Woods were the dimmest shade, or that the Waters
were profoundly deep; But that over all Rocks, Wood,
and Water, brooded the Spirit of Repose, and the silent
energy of Nature stirred the Soul to it inmost depths.

-Thomas Cole

Note: Thanks to N. Dalrymple, one of my daughters, for her wonderful paper on Nutmeg. Excerpts are included in this article.

xxii. Osmanthus

LATIN NAME: OSMANTHUS FRAGRANS

FAMILY NAME: OLEACEAE

"Extreme fragrance", heady and full-bodied euphoria, and complex aphrodisiac qualities describe some of this Deva's personality. According to history China has cultivated Osmanthus for thousands of years. As an evergreen, She again calls forth Eternal Life, the desire for it and the seeking of it. Some call Her a large shrub, others a tree, growing from around 10' to 20'. Her flowers are the mesmerizing secret to her fame. They can be white, gold, silver or orange, exuding a color energy. The intoxicating fragrance added to Her, creates an orb of light similar to the Morpho butterflies' blue wings. The essence, in the form of an absolute, is usually produced from the gold-orange blossoms.

Her ability to perpetuate Divine Self Love is phenomenal. Her ability to speak of calming to the soul, unconditional love, and patience to our heart-mind is like a white dove who wakes you in the morning with a nostalgic cooing, bidding you to once again get up, shake yourself free, and journey with happiness through a new day.

Osmanthus blooms in the fall in China, and the other countries in which she resides, including Japan, and the Himalayas. This reminds me, that when many Tree and Plant species are losing their leaves, she is bringing forth beautiful life and unparalleled aroma to Her surroundings. It is said that the valleys where She blooms in the autumn are like a vortex opening into paradise. The people who live in such surroundings seem to float through their daily journeys without effort and with smiles of orgasmic pleasure. In China, She is among the ten most famous flowers.

Osmanthus gorgeous flower actually produces a fragrant olive for fruit, known as sweet olive, fragrant olive or tea olive. Medicinally, She reduces phlegm in the lungs and throat, opening the channels of our physical, emotional and spiritual bodies to purer oxygen. How we all cry out in these times for more pure physical, emotional and spiritual oxygen! Osmanthus will help clear the air of pollutants, pathogens and the like. She aids in moving static blood and in promoting life and energy in our circulatory system. To take one drop of Her in a glass of water as a libation is to feel Her course through your veins giving you renewed strength and vigor. I am sitting here writing this to you as She is on my upper lip, my crown chakra, whispering to me Her message. She says. "My message is almost complete except for this one last tidbit... do you really remember how much love we Flowers and Trees bestow upon you everyday?" Do you really remember how much we love to live on this Earth to bless all beings, including your precious species? Do you remember how we have given you an example from the beginning about staying in harmony and peace with Creator and Earth Mother? We love you, we love you, we love you. From me, Osmanthus."

A Flower's fragrance declares to all the world that it is fertile,

Available, and desirable, it's sex organs oozing with nectar.

Its smell reminds us in vestigial ways of fertility, vigor, life-force, all.

The optimism, expectancy, and passionate bloom of youth.

We inhale its ardent aroma and, no matter what our ages, we feel

Young and nubile in a world aflame with desire.

-Diane Ackerman, *A Natural History Of The Senses*, 1990, p.13

xxiii. Peppermint

LATIN NAME: MENTHA PIPERITA

FAMILY NAME: LAMIACEAE

Is there anyone in any part of the world that has not heard in his or her own language about the mint family and in particular, **PEPPERMINT?** Well, let's talk about Her a little and renew our appreciation for this most amazing gift to us from Mother Earth. Her smell is enough to invoke ancient memories of relaxation, clarity and peace. She is a famous nervine, calming and cooling us down spiritually, emotionally and physically. Many people, when they first really start using Her in the form of an essential essence, think they experience an extreme heat reaction, and often say, "Oh my God, it is hot!" No, She is not a producer of heat. She is actually a heavy-duty coolant, that until you experience Her enough, the great coldness of Her actually feels hot like dry ice. Your mind has to build a memory for what Mother Earth's secrets are, this being one of them: being so cold, She feels hot.

The name *Mentha* means "mind" or "spirit" in Latin, and has pointed us to the crispness of this essence and the many levels that She addresses for living beings, here on planet Earth. There is a place on the ancient walls of Edfu, the Egyptian Temple dedicated to the God Horus, where the mint family is a part of the secret recipes for spiritual perfumes used in meditation, worship and ritual. If you are studying sacred geometry, She will enhance your remembrance about the Source of all. In French history, the mint family has been spoken of as extremely open hearted, and so frank as to perhaps be detrimental. Could it be that peppermint, as well as other mints, (like spearmint-*Mentha spicata*), will continue to be prime movers in opening our hearts to listen and speak our truths, without masks and onion layers? I believe so. Mint signifies, "exalted love" and in many cultures is considered to be an exquisite aphrodisiac.

There are at least 30 dis-eases that peppermint can and will address on all three levels of this life and the list is still growing. She reduces fevers, is a digestive sedative, and creates clarity. She can eradicate certain headaches, and helps cleanse the liver. In summer She is wonderful in a glass of water for a sense of smoothness and cooling. Common sense is always the theme for life, and the use of peppermint is not excluded. However, fear is not akin or equivalent to true common sense but WISDOM is. Babies, who weigh so little, of course cannot take the same amount as can adults. Why is it that humans can't figure out some of these simple things? "Read my lips" in order to wisely use the mint family for children. But, you know what? You really do know these things already. I am here to just help you remember these truths. Now stay as fresh and real as PEPPERMINT.

Stand tall and proud

Sink your roots deeply into the Earth

Reflect the Light of a Greater Source

Think long term

Go out on a limb

Remember your place among all living Beings

Embrace with Joy the changing seasons

For each yields its own abundance

The energy and birth of Spring

The growth and contentment of Summer

The Wisdom to let go of leaves in the Fall

The rest and quiet renewal of Winter

-Ilan Shamir, *Advice From A Tree*

XXIV. RHODODENDRON

LATIN NAME: RHODODENDRON ANTHOPOGON

FAMILY NAME: LAURACEAE

Rhodo means Rose, **Dendron** means Tree... *Rhododendron anthopogon* is an Angel of particular interest to me. I traveled to Nepal in the early part of 2005 and talked to Her. The essence comes from a holy part of Earth Mother, and is used extensively by the Hindu and Buddhist peoples, among others. From ancient times, She has been the friend of many to provide emotional uplifting and courage along the pathway of life's many challenges. Her fragrance has a most uncanny way of taking one back to ancient lives that we have experienced in order to review and observe our present state of affairs in the life we are now living. She provides an opportunity for shape shifting, and re-examining what is most important right now for you and me.

In the physical realm, She has a direct affect on our blood capillaries, which denotes so much importance when we consider the condition of our terrain that encompasses our very life's blood. How freely, how easily, how full the blood flows through the corridors to reach its destination and work its miracles. Likewise, in the emotional and spiritual realms, She facilitates the same function along the corridors of our lives' journeys, helping to give the possibility of unobstructed flow for a full and beautiful life. An actual "happily-ever-after reality," potential can be realized. In meditation She is famous in such locales as Nepal amongst the many masters and masters-to-be for the above-mentioned gifts that She bestows so freely. Along with this, She helps harmonize the liver, kidney and spleen functions, which again work together for the vibrancy of the blood. Remember, "The Life is in The Blood," which always denotes our health on the three levels we experience here on Earth Mother- spiritually, emotionally, and physically.

The Nepalese people comment that this most sacred Angel energizes their whole being in a most unique and deep way. However, this result does not happen without desiring to work on our stuff and create a new and exciting story over and above the old stories that no longer serve us and, in fact, do not represent who we really are any more! She is well known for Her ability to open doors so that you may find and know who and where your spiritual family is. The Rose Tree of Love bids you a blessing in experiencing Her.

In my garden there is a large place for sentiment.
My garden of Flowers is also my garden of thoughts
and dreams. The thoughts grow as freely as the Flow-
ers, and the dreams are as beautiful.
-Abram L. Urban

xxv. Rose hip *MOSQUETA*- NUT OIL

LATIN NAME: ROSA RUBIGINOSA

FAMILY NAME: **ROSACEAE**

There are several nut oils about which I have written about in the past; Rose Hip is one of Them. I cannot ever speak enough about Her. As a nut oil, She is at the top of the list. We have blessed so many people with the encouragement to use Her, and they just rave about Her. In Western Europe, there is a huge push to put Her in all kinds of natural cosmetics. I would like to tell you though, using it 'neat' is the way to go. Our Rose Hip comes from our farmer in Chile. It is so pure and smells wonderful. We use it topically for all sorts of skin dryness, and dermatitis issues. People are constantly complaining about dryness in their genital areas. Their anal sphincters get dry and sore even without hemorrhoids and they ask us what they can use to remedy the problem. Rose Hips Seed Oil is our number one recommendation.. Applying a liberal amount on your whole genital and rectal area after a shower every day will see worthwhile results in just a few days. Be aware that it will stain white clothing so use common sense. I had a gentleman complain that people thought he had not cleaned himself in weeks due to stains on clothing around his crotch. Maybe he was bit too liberal. HELLO! We Americans sit a lot just in the work place, let alone in front of the TV, Computer, Car, etc. She is a skin regenerator because of the essential fatty acids' role in the formation and reformation of membranes. She also stimulates collagen production, which can literally fill acne pit holes over a 6-month period of committed treatment.

Recently, when visiting South America, Cynthia and I were amazed at the amount of passionate work that goes into the pressing of the tiny Rose Hip Seeds. We watched the beautiful red oil pour out of the press into the holding containers. It was just stunning!

Rose Hip Seed Oil is wonderful for dry, scaled, dull, fissured skin, hyper-pigmented skin and post surgical scars. Taken internally, She will facilitate healing of an inflamed liver, intestinal disorders and ulcers. She will coat the colon, and aid peristaltic action and bowel movements. She aids in balancing blood pressure, cholesterol levels. The sympathetic nervous system also loves Her.

Used in concert with but at separate times with pure essential essences, She will speed up the healing process greatly.

Animals love Her also. I have treated mange and various injuries with great success. The animals love Her smell and lick and lick the treated area. That is wonderful because they have the opportunity to take it internally as well. The praises could go on and on; but folks remember, we are talking about a magnificent Nut

Oil here, not an essential essence. May you rejoice, as we do, in using Her and creating a relationship with Her.

> *Looking like a Pomegranate, I stared to gaze upon*
> *this Red Ball,*
>> *Called Rose Hip*
>> *Full of Seeds so small*
>> *Only to realize that I took for granted*
>> *That the Seeds within heard the call*
>> *To come out and play with humans*
>> *And have a ball.*

-B. B. Kapp

XXVI. SAINT JOHN'S WORT-*KLAMATH*

LATIN NAME: HYPERICUM PERFORATUM

FAMILY NAME: **HYPERICACEAE**

A queen of queens, this Deva has a very ancient history of working with humans. Native Americans once ate Her just like acorns. Nations from East to West, among our indigenous sisters and brothers, used Her continuously. According to history almost every country in the world had Her for the asking.

Did you know that according to the latest statistics, about 75% of the human population relies on the Tree and Plant Kingdoms to facilitate their healing– spiritually, emotionally and physiologically? In past years, humans knew about several hundred Trees and Plants that would cleanse the blood. An astute indigenous person knew in excess of 1,000 remedies available from Trees and Plants. We are again on a fast track to revive this sacred relationship that is precious on all levels. St. John's Wort is one remedy still largely in use. There is a 2,500-year written recorded history on this very Deva. The gifts that She possesses are awesome, to say the least. She is used for addiction issues, liver protector, anti cancer, heart dis-eases, glandular fevers, gastritis, hemorrhoids, Herpes 1 & 2 (simplex sores), testicle pain, prostatitis, tissue and wound healer, post surgical scars, immune stimulant, UTI's, urinary incontinence and Lyme dis-ease. The list goes on.

Emotionally, She has a long history of helping humans with depression, without exception. When She first received attention in the U.S., the allopathic articles, stated that She was only effective for mild depression. This was only a smoke screen to discourage people from using Her. First of all, very few allopathic advocates know anything about herbs or essential essences, much less use them, which bring about feelings, experiences and explorations. Let it be known that, when She is pure, She can clear all levels of depression with no side effects. This does not mean that one can project all their problems away from themselves. No, no, She teaches, just like all of the other essences, that YOU take responsibility for your own story, journey, and actions, including the roots of depression. She will bring you to the door of understanding. ONLY YOU CAN WALK THROUGH THAT DOOR AND CREATE A NEW STORY FOR YOURSELF; THERE IS NO COERCION FROM HER – JUST LOVE AND HELP. There is no such thing as the "magical pink pill", never has been, never will be, and essential essences are not in this category either. Essential essences when pure are beyond powerful. The Tree and Plant Kingdom work, but They always let you make the final decision and take responsibility for your own actions and life.

Spiritually, She is an Angel of the highest order. I have seen Her Blossoms as Yellow Stars in my dreams– swirling around and around, spreading healing and love Earth-wide. She has told me that She is a gift from the constellation Orion. The yellow blossoms point to the exhilaration, exuberance, and happiness that She bestows upon those that heed Her beckoning. She knows extremely deep, ancient secrets that She brings to the table for you and me. Coming from Orion, She has the stamina, patience, and endurance to stay with you through thick or thin, lovingly helping you find your way through this dense plane and maze. She has traveled far, on the wings of Her ancestors. She has not forgotten who She is, nor from where She comes. She knows that She is an extension of Her family, pointing us all to a higher consciousness to which She is so-o-o-o connected, and She so longs for us to catch the vision. This awareness, Oh, Ancient One, melts my heart with your great, great Love.

> *"Uo 'Ia I ka manai ho'okahl"*
> *Strung like Flowers on the same Lei needle.*
> *Married.*
> -Hawaiian Proverbs

XXVII. SPRUCES THE BLACK, BLUE, NORWAY, RED, SITKA, WHITE SISTERS

LATIN NAME: PICEA MARIANA OR NIGRA, PICEA PUNGENS, PICEA ABIES, PICEA RUBRUM, PICEA SITKA, PICEA GLAUCA

FAMILY NAME: PINACEAE

Considering the times, which we are living in, when humans are facing an ever more pronounced choice between Fear or Divine Love, I would like to comment on some very old Grandmothers. They are Wise Wisdom Teachers called the **Spruces**. They are considered part of the Conifer Family. They were the very first Trees that were here on Mother, way before the Humans walked here. Today they live around 500-800 years, and have much experience in weathering the storms of life here. They have had a long time to view many stories, the beginnings and the outcomes. They usually live in high elevations where the extremes are more vivid, the air so fresh and clean.

Wisdom of the Earth carries 6 species of Spruce. Why? As a Father of nine beautiful children, I found many unique blessings with each child. Yes, many similarities, but each, oh so different. This is the same with the Spruces. The gifts of one work wonderfully with the gifts of another, if we only look, feel, experience, explore, taste, and touch with our inner heart and vision. This would also invovle observing Them on a quantum level. They help us to view life from a different, magnificent perspective. We also have the physical dimension where so much human energy has been placed for far too long. Now slowly yet steadily, we are reawakening to the realization that the Spiritual and Emotional parts of us create the biology of our physical bodies.

Let's talk about These Sisters. *Picea mariana* or *nigra*, colloquially known as Spruce, Black, etc. are names that have meaning, not just coincidence, because some botanist decided that this Spruce looks like it is more black than the red or blue ones. Mother Earth gives humans a lot of freedom in many areas, but know that She operates only from Divine Love and has unknown capabilities to influence any and all decisions made by us. This even includes naming things. Of course, the Tree and Plant Kingdom shares this ability with Mother also.

I would like to summarize that my experiences working with these different Spruces are the following: Black works with our shadow or dark side in the realms of duality. Blue works with our 5th chakra and our voice. Norway works with our 3rd chakra and our self-esteem, worth, purpose. Red works with our true passions and how can we know what they are. Sitka works with our 4th chakra and how delicious it is to feel and live in our hearts all the time. White works with the 7th, and beyond chakras to open up our God Consciousness. With Their strong life force They address on the physical plane, stimulation of the immune system, our life force (chi) in every way. They address our respiratory systems on every level, parasites on many levels, and are highly anti-infectious, anti-viral and anti-aging. You can take one of These Sisters and do a complete liver detox, over a period of a month. They have also become famous in addressing arthritis pain. They have natural cortisone chemotypes and properties. Let me share more on arthritis. We now know that arthritis is a long enduring latent virus that grows very slowly. Then one day we wake up and, "Uncle Arthur", knocks on our door. Uncle Arthur says, "Hey there, you have been asleep for a long time, mindlessly misusing and abusing your precious body." My Blessed Father never experienced, "Uncle Arthur" in all of his 85 years. You don't have to either. The Spruces are here to help and my own body has been thankful for Their expertise many times. Pulled muscles, low back pain, knee and joint aches due to yoga or pilates.

The Spruce Family is one of my dearest friends. They continue to teach me as I use them constantly on my patients and myself. Believe in them, have a relationship with them and explore them. Yes, you can do this by reading books, such as this one, but I am actually speaking more about experiencing Them through an intimate relationship, day by day, year after year. Their Love and Wisdom will shine through you to others. You will see the groundedness that the Spruce Family stimulates in a most Gentle and Enduring Way.

The Forests are the flags of Nature. They appeal to all and awaken inspiring universal feelings. Enter the Forest and the boundaries of nations are forgotten. It may be that some time an immortal Pine will be the flag of a United Peaceful World.

-Enos A. Mills- Hawaiian Proverbs

XXVIII.
SUGANDHA KOKILA

LATIN NAME: CINNAMOMUM GLAUCESCENS

MEISSN

FAMILY NAME: LAURACEAE

From the berries of this exquisite Deva comes an essence that to us is best described as **White Cinnamon**. She is Yin in nature, which is so unlike Her sisters, Cinnamon Bark or Cassia Bark. I have been using Her directly undiluted on my skin for scratches, wounds and skin blemishes. It has been clearing up my scratches and cuts very quickly. With regard to the blemishes, I am doing a case study on myself. In Nepal She is known for Her medicinal abilities for facilitating healing for all kinds of skin diseases. She is a new essence for this country. I had heard about Her for some time when traveling overseas, but now, within the last 3 years, we have added Her to our portfolio of essences.

Her smell is pleasant, medium light and fun to be around.

What do I mean? She is playful like a child that awakens the inner child inside of us very easily. This I find very intriguing and challenging. I believe She knows how to address the emotional and spiritual outer layers of discomfort, which we often experience. You know what I mean... those little irritations that come our way without us knowing, many times, where they actually came from. In a playful way She brings us to the awareness that no matter how strong we think we are, SHE IS A FRIEND IN TIME OF NEED. She is so precious.

In Nepal She also has addressed general discomfort in all areas of pain and unrest. The berries, which represent the creative fruit of **Sugandha Kokila**, have captured our attention when used for cerebral ischemia. Ischemia is associated with poor blood supply to any organ or part, often accompanied by pain or organ dysfunction. In areas of heart dis-ease, She is well known for aiding the physical heart. This includes heart spasms, heartburn, coronaritis, and coronary thrombosis. I find She increases clarity and alertness in a gentle but enduring way. When our lungs are aggravated from heavy accumulation of debris from any dimension, causing anxiety, She gently lays Her hand on the dis-ease and brings relief. I am finding that she facilitates anti-viral, anti-fungal, anti-bacterial, and anti-parasitic actions in a new way for us, which we are exploring at present. A White Light She is. There is evidence that She addresses the 7th and 8th chakras in really reaching upward to lessen dense blockages. The lighter, higher blockages are often more difficult to detect and work with because they are so illusive but real just the same. "I stimulate the pineal gland," She says. A powerful angel... I desire to commune with Her more and more.

"... the very process of the restoring the land to health is the process through which we become attuned to Nature and, through Nature, with ourselves.

Restoration forestry, therefore, is both the means and the end, for as we learn how to restore the Forest, we heal the Forest, and as we heal the Forest, we heal ourselves.

-Chris Maser, *Forest Primeva*

xxix. TANSY, WILD

LATIN NAME: TANACETUM VULGARE

FAMILY NAME: ASTERACEAE

Exploring this Deva was most interesting. First, I would like to share with you an experience from one of our Level 1 students. "We settled down in the morning of the second day of class for a meditative journey. With eyes closed, I felt a finger saturated with an oil of unknown origin planted directly on my third eye. Whoa! I was immediately transported out of my body, a yellow halo crowning my head. I was so moved by this experience that almost immediately, hot tears started to run down my cheeks. The connection to something so much greater than me was profound in this instant. I felt nurtured, loved, embraced and cleansed of earthly thoughts, and of any of the daily thoughts of insufficiency that run through one's head. Divine light and love were mine, and I was almost euphoric... I felt there was a direct cord of yellow light pulling me up and tenderly holding me. It was as if Mother Love was present. It was absolutely powerful! I felt an incredible release of my heart and an opening of my heart space. It was for me, a true connection to this Deva. At the time, I had no notion of who She was.

We came out of this meditation and I was this Deva's new best friend. She had whispered directly to my higher self what I needed, even if I in the physical body did not know it. I could hardly speak. I was told that this was **Tansy Wild.** I was delighted to my core at this connection and even if I had not learned one more thing during this training, this experience would have been well worth the trip."[1]

Medicinally, Wild Tansy is a relative of Feverfew, which is used in aiding pain and fever. The flowers are pungent and are wonderful for ridding one of bugs. It has been used as a preservative for storing food, for eliminating parasitic worms, and as an herb for cooking.

In translation from Latin, *tanacetum* means death, from the Romans, and in Greek, "land of the dead." It keeps worms, maggots and other parasites at bay during the grieving and burying process, but also on a spiritual level, death to my old self (ego) and an opening into Divine light. There is a record of Native history (1854) where Tansy had been used in a sweat lodge to purify after a death rite (Chaluilla Indians, San Diego, CA). Other medicinal uses range from poultice application of leaves to teas, cakes used for ridding one of worms, hysteria, kidney weaknesses, fever, nervousness and mild stomach disorders. Tansy supports the immune system and appears to tonify the entire system. She is highly anti-viral. She helps create a positive attitude and a general feeling of well being. She has a great ability to take you on a spiritual journey without causing the hallucinations that such concoctions as Ayawausca and others do.

Today, many persons consider Tansy a weed and a nuisance, for She grows profusely alongside the roads and in fields where she is common. Due to a lack of understanding some even spray Her with weed killer to get rid of Her. The thought of Her being a nuisance to some at the side of the road, I couldn't help but think, "Nuisance, because the Divine is trying to get your attention!" And "Man usually interferes with anything that is wild and uncontrolled by mass consciousness, so we'll kill it! Spray Her, cut Her, and destroy Her, or try to." So many of us run from the very things that will be our greatest helpers. She is calling to all road travelers, "Please come kiss the face of the divine within you, I will show you how." Wild and free. Cleansed and loved. Could one ask for more? I think not.

> *Laughter when a gauzy, purple butterfly,*
> *Softly tilts a golden Flower,*
> *It's cool wings ease the Summer flame*
> *As Laughter soothes a troubled hour.*
> -Courtney E. Cottam

---

[1] Thank you, R.D. Kooy, a student. She gets credit for parts of this article.

xxx. TARRAGON

LATIN NAME: ARTEMISIA DRACUNCULUS

FAMILY NAME: ASTERACEAE

Tarragon is one of the many fabulous plants from the *Asteraceae botanical* (family formerly called the *Compositae* family). Often aromatic, the Asteraceae family is the most evolved in the planet world.

Tarragon can be used with excellent results topically, rectally, vaginally, by inhalation and internally. We have made a wonderful tea with pure honey from Tarragon that soothes many stomach issues. With a little know-how one can use Her to facilitate healing in many areas. It is used for spasmodic colitis, dysmenorrheal and premenstrual pain, PMS, anorexia, allergies, neuromuscular cramps, nausea, hiccups, aerophagia, flatulence, and spasmophilia. She is anti-viral, anti-carcinogenic and works to facilitate healing in kidney infections. Layering it topically with a sequence of Basil, *(Oclmum basilicum)*, Tarragon, and then Basil again, will bring about fast results for most levels of colon discomfort and imbalance. Tarragon applied on the skin by itself can be potentially skin-sensitive. As always, common sense teaches us to always do a test patch when you are experiencing a new essence. On the emotional level, She will address anxiety, frustration and unresolved blockages, which SHAMANICALLY bridges with physiological colon problems. Spiritually, She will help aid opening and healing of your cosmic digestion as you walk your journey.

Today, the whole issue of constipation is huge and we would do ourselves a great service to listen to our stomach dis-eases and feel what is going on physically, emotionally and spiritually. Even for menopause She stands out as a Rite of Passage essence. She will unite with other passage essences such as Frankincense, Sandalwood, Asarium canadensis, Ginger Lily and help you in the transition. Her ancient name refers to dragon, and why not. She can calm the colon dragon in a special way. The colon is also linked to our eyesight. She is Yin/Yang in nature and will tenderly bond with you in a warm and tenacious way. Her calmness and serenity will become part of you very quickly.

From the beginning, man was a Being
that sustains his life through eating.
Within his body is a long friend that is called Colon.
When Tarragon communes with the body, Colon rejoices.
Here is friend that promotes harmony for Sister Colon.

-B. B. Kapp

XXXI. VETIVER

LATIN NAME: VETIVERIA ZIZANOIDES

FAMILY NAME: POACEAE

Vetiver is a most exquisite Deva that is becoming more known in the U.S. Vetiver is famous in Asia and around the Equator. She is extremely Yin, which means mild, non-irritating, cool to warm in temperature, and gentle. The essence comes from the root system, which is huge and complex. The size of the roots is usually as large, if not larger, than the grass itself above the ground. She is one that often calls me to use first when treating clients when I desire to layer more Yang (warm to hot) essences immediately on top of Her.

She is known as a stimulator of the red blood cells, whose primary function is to transport oxygen throughout the body (though I am sure She has other important blood functions that we are still remembering). Shamanically, Vetiver is a stimulant for your very life force, chi‒ to reveal your passions in life so that you can perceive your journey more clearly. She calls forth your deepest passions for gentleness, kindness and compassion as She nurtures your physical body with Her warming, velvety consistency. As an aphrodisiac, She lovingly opens dusty cobweb closets in your heart that have been shut by you. Vetiver is very friendly and gentle with those humans who have chosen the realm of frigidity and have forgotten how to trust themselves and fall in love with themselves once again.

She aids all sorts of dermatological problems, which reveals Her desire to protect the shields that surround each one of us in loving empathy. She is gentle enough to use in sensitive areas, such as the underarms, making Her a wonderful deodorant. My wife and I use Her most every day. A true friend of those with insomnia, she comforts us into sleep physically. Emotionally and spiritually you can dream into reality the grandest version of yourself and be rejuvenated for the next level of your journey here on this dense plane.

She is a pancreatic stimulant and can aid in post partum depression. "Rubbing Me on a pregnant woman's tummy prepares the little one for the earthy vibrations that they are about to encounter," She whispers. Then She compassionately looks at all those on prescribed tranquilizers, and comments, "I will ground you to the earth, and you can say goodbye to such harmful drugs; I will show you a better way that will bring happiness to your body, soul and spirit." Vetiver also aids all levels of liver congestion, which equates to helping us to flush out all of our baggage so that we can move forward, unimpeded, on our journey. Vetiver is continually unfolding Her secrets of love and joy in these stressful times for all who care to have a most extraordinary experience.

Until man duplicates a blade of Grass,
Nature can laugh at his so called scientific knowledge.

-Thomas Edison

BIOGRAPHY

Barry B. Kapp

About The Author

Barry B. Kapp, Master Medicinal Aromatherapist and founder of ***Wisdom of the Earth***, has studied aromatherapy internationally. He shares his experiences, explorations, feelings and knowing in seminars, workshops and consultations worldwide. He was introduced to the Wonder and Power, Harmony and Joy of the Natural World by both his Mother and Father at the age of three. Fifty-nine years have gone by and his passion is still the same. He shares the Wisdom and Love from the Tree and Plant Kingdom to his own species, the humans. He has had many human mentors but believes that his Tree and Plant and Animal friends have influenced him even more.

Barry is a retired dairy and cash crop farmer. He resides near Sedona, AZ. with his wife, Cynthia. They have twelve children and seven grandchildren between them.

Wisdom of the Earth, a Medicinal Aromatherpy company sells only pure single hand-poured in ceremony essential essences. Barry and his wife, Cynthia are avalible for consultations and treatments. Barry teaches certification courses internationally. For information about classes, treatments and schedules, go to:

www.WisdomoftheEarth.com

or mail Barry at: barryessence373@yahoo.com

Notes

Notes

Notes

Notes

Notes

Notes

Notes

Notes